Indian Melo...

Mélodies indiennes
Indische Melodien

for violin
pour violon
für Violine

Candida Connolly

with accompanying CD produced in association with the
Bharatiya Vidya Bhavan, UK Centre

disque compact d'accompagnement produit en association avec le
Centre Bharatiya Vidya Bhavan (U.K.)

mit Begleit-CD hergestellt in Zusammenarbeit mit dem
Bharatiya Vidya Bhavan, UK Centre

ED 12732

I would like to dedicate this book to my parents Robin and Anne Denniston,
whose deep love of music was instilled in me, and my husband Shane, for his constant
love and support.

Je dédie cet ouvrage à mes parents, Robin et Anne Denniston, qui m'ont transmis leur
profond amour de la musique, et à mon mari Shane, pour son amour et son constant
soutien.

Ich möchte dieses Buch meinen Eltern Robin und Anne Denniston widmen,
die mir ihre tiefe Liebe zur Musik weitergegeben haben, und meinem Ehemann Shane
für seine dauerhafte Liebe und Unterstützung.

ED 12732
British Library Cataloguing-in-Publication Data.
A catalogue record for this book is available from the British Library
ISMN M-2201-2232-3

French translation: Agnès Ausseur
German translation: Ute Corleis
Cover design and page layout by www.adamhaystudio.com
Illustrations by Chris Price (cover and p. 20)
Music setting and page layout by Jack Thompson
Printed in Germany S& Co. 7747

Indian Melodies
Mélodies indiennes / Indische Melodien

Acknowledgements

In the preparation of this book, I have needed assistance both on the practical side of music-making and in the theoretical background to Indian music, North and South.

In the field of South Indian, or Karnatic music, I freely acknowledge the encouragement and practical help I received from Professor T. V. Gopalakrishnan who also graciously consented to write the foreword. I am eternally grateful to my teacher in India, Vidwan N. Gopalakrishna Iyer and to my very first teacher of Karnatic music, Sri Kadri Gopalnath. I am also most grateful for the critical eye of Dr Askaran Sharma.

At the Bharatiya Vidya Bhavan's UK Centre in London I received much help from their resident South Indian percussion (mridangam) teacher Sri M. Balachandar. I was moreover delighted by the help his leading pupil Pirashanna Thevarajah gave in the CD that accompanies this book. The Bhavan's resident teacher of violin, Sri Balu Raguraman afforded great help in the preparation of the CD as did Sri Sivaganesh, my own teacher of violin. I would also like to thank Sm. Sivasakti Sivanesan, resident teacher of Karnatic music.

In the field of North Indian music I received unstinting help and encouragement from Pandit Vishwa Prakash, Resident teacher of Hindustani (North Indian) vocal music. Also, extremely helpful has been the Bhavan's resident sitar teacher Sri Vijaykumar Jagtap.

My great thanks go to Dr John Marr, Bhavan's teacher of Karnatic theory, for his great knowledge, support and guidance.

I also thank the students with whom I have used this material, particularly those from the Gloucester Academy of Music and Performing Arts, my violin students from Whitbourne Primary School and Megan Evans for her artistic prowess.

Candida Connolly

Foreword

This book seeks to present North and South Indian music in staff notation to interested and discerning young western minds and whet their appetite for more. This is in no way a comprehensive work but it is a good way for a westerner to get an experience of Indian music in a practical manner.

Compositions from North and South Indian music have been selected to show the two different musical approaches which come from the same tradition of raga and tala. These approaches generate aesthetic and creative appeal in their own unique ways.

The Indian raga is elaborated through improvised phrases which are called *alapana* (or *alap* in North Indian music) followed by songs set in a rhythmic framework which show lyrical content of a devotional nature. Melody is produced by the tonal movement within a raga which is based on principles of consonance (or blend of notes), vibrations and overtones – whatever goes to make a sound. The *gamaka* or ornamentation of Indian music conforms to these tonal values in both Hindustani and Karnatic music. This is achieved with the background support of a drone.

The items in this book are representative of different modes and musical forms so as to appeal to beginners and help them to study and graduate towards performance levels. The tonal movement in Indian music may be unfamiliar to the western ear, however crossing the divide is possible. My work with western music students in Europe and America as well as India and with Indian music students of western instruments such as the violin and saxophone has demonstrated an ability to adapt and transform both the musical ear and the musical 'machinery'. To understand the perception of Indian music through the bending and inflexions of notes can be aided in part through the written medium, but mostly will be gained through the ear, for which the accompanying CD will be of help.

I highly commend Candida's work which comes as part of her commitment and many years' study of Indian music.

Prof. T. V. Gopalakrishnan
Academy of Indian Music and Arts
Chennai

Remerciements

La réalisation de ce recueil a nécessité pour moi aide et assistance importantes tant du point de vue pratique de l'exécution des musiques indiennes du nord et du sud de l'Inde que de la théorie les soutenant.

Dans le domaine de la musique de l'Inde méridionale, ou musique carnatique, je suis très reconnaissante au professeur T.V.Gopalakrishnan de ses encouragements et de l'aide pratique dont il m'a fait bénéficier ainsi que de son aimable acceptation de rédiger l'avant-propos de ce recueil. Ma gratitude infinie va, en Inde, à mon maître Vidwan N. Gopalakrishna Iyer et à mon tout premier professeur de musique karnatique Sri Kadri Gopalnath, ainsi qu'à l'oeil critique du Dr. Askaran Sharma.

Au Centre Bharatiya Vidya Bhavan de Londres, j'ai reçu l'aide précieuse de Sri M. Balachandar, professeur résident de percussion d'Inde méridionale (*mridangam*). J'ai été, de plus, enchantée de l'assistance apportée par son principal disciple, Pirashanna Thevarajah, à la réalisation du disque compact accompagnant ce recueil, qui doit également beaucoup à Sri Balu Raguraman, professeur de violon résident, et à Sri Sivaganesh, mon propre professeur de violon. Je désire aussi remercier Mme Sivasakti Sivanesan, professeur résident de musique carnatique.

Du côté de la musique du nord de l'Inde, j'ai profité de l'aide généreuse et des encouragements de Pandit Vishwa Prakash, professeur résident de musique vocale hindoustanaise (du nord de l'Inde). De même me furent extrêmement utiles les conseils de Sri Vijaykumar Jagtap, professeur résident de sitar.

Toute ma gratitude s'adresse au Dr John Marr, professeur de théorie carnatique au Centre Bhavan, pour son immense savoir, son soutien et sa direction.

Je remercie également les étudiants avec lesquels j'ai expérimenté ce matériel, en particulier ceux de l'Academy of Music and Performing Arts de Gloucester, mes élèves de violon de l'école primaire de Whitbourne et Megan Evans de son talent artistique.

Candida Connolly

Avant-propos

Ce recueil propose la transcription sur portée de musiques originaires du nord et du sud de l'Inde et se destine aux jeunes esprits occidentaux intéressés et perspicaces afin de satisfaire leur appétit de nouveauté. Il ne s'agit aucunement d'un ouvrage exhaustif mais il s'avère une excellente manière pour un Occidental d'aborder la musique indienne de manière pratique.

Cette sélection de musique indienne du nord et du sud de l'Inde résume les deux approches musicales divergentes provenant de la même tradition du *raga* et du *tala*. Chacune de ces deux tendances offre en propre un attrait esthétique et créatif unique.

Le raga indien s'élabore au moyen de phrases improvisées, appelées *alapana* (ou *alap* dans la musique du Nord), suivies de chants évoluant dans un cadre rythmique et au contenu lyrique de nature religieuse. La mélodie se forme à partir du mouvement interne du raga fondé sur des principes de consonances (ou de mélanges de notes), de vibrations et d'harmoniques – tous éléments concourant à produire un son. Le *gamaka* ou ornementation de la musique indienne se conforme à ces valeurs tonales, tant dans la musique hindoustanaise que dans la musique carnatique, avec le soutien d'un bourdon.

Les pièces contenues dans ce recueil, représentatives de différents modes et formes musicales, sont accessibles à des débutants afin de les aider dans leur étude et les amener à des niveaux divers d'exécution. Le contour tonal de la musique indienne peut se révéler déroutant pour l'oreille occidentale, mais il est cependant possible de surmonter cette dissemblance. Le travail que j'ai effectué avec des étudiants musiciens occidentaux en Europe, en Amérique et en Inde, ainsi qu'avec des étudiants musiciens indiens travaillant des instruments occidentaux, tels que le violin et saxophone, a montré la capacité de l'oreille musicale et des « mécanismes » musicaux à s'adapter et à se transformer. On peut partiellement faciliter par le support écrit l'abord de la démarche de perception de la musique indienne fondée sur la distorsion et l'inflexion des notes, mais celle-ci doit s'effectuer par l'oreille et le CD d'accompagnement y aidera.

Je recommande vivement l'ouvrage de Candida Connolly, témoignage de son engagement et de ses nombreuses années d'études de la musique indienne.

Pr T.V.Gopalakrishnan
Académie de la musique et des arts indiens
(*Chennai*)

Danksagung

Bei der Vorbereitung dieses Buches brauchte ich sowohl Hilfe auf Seiten der Musikpraxis, als auch hinsichtlich des theoretischen Hintergrunds der Musik in Nord- und Südindien.

Auf dem Gebiet der südindischen oder karnatischen Musik erkenne ich freimütig die Ermutigung und praktische Hilfe an, die ich von Professor T.V. Gopalakrishnan erhielt, der sich dankenswerter Weise auch dazu bereit erklärte, das Vorwort zu schreiben. Meinem Lehrer Vidwan N. Gopalakrishna Iyer in Indien sowie meinem allerersten karnatischen Musiklehrer Sri Kadri Gopalnath werde ich für immer dankbar sein.

Am Bharatiya Vidya Bhavan UK Centre in London wurde ich sehr von deren südindischem Perkussionslehrer (Mridangam) Sri M. Balachandar unterstützt. Darüber hinaus war ich begeistert von der Hilfe, die ich von seinem Meisterschüler Pirashanna Thevarajah bei der Erstellung der Begleit-CD bekam.

Der Violinlehrer des Bhavan, Sri Balu Raguraman, leistete große Hilfe bei der Vorbereitung der CD, genauso wie Sri Sivaganesh, mein eigener Violinlehrer.

Auf dem Gebiet der nordindischen Musik erhielt ich von Pandit Vishwa Prakash, Lehrer der hindustanischen (nordindischen) Vokalmusik, uneingeschränkte Hilfe und Ermutigung. Ebenfalls äußerst hilfreich war der Sitar-Lehrer des Bhavan, Sri Vijaykumar Jagtap. Außerdem bin ich Dr. Askaran Sharma für seine kritische Durchsicht des Manuscript sehr dankbar.

Großer Dank gebührt auch Dr. John Marr, Bhavans Lehrer der karnatischen Musiktheorie, für sein großes Wissen, seine Unterstützung und Führung. Ohne ihn wäre dieses Buch deutlich weniger sachkundig geworden.

Bedanken möchte ich mich auch bei den Studenten, an denen ich dieses Material ausprobiert habe, besonders bei denen von der Gloucester Academy of Music and Performing Arts, meinen Violinstudenten von der Grundschule in Whitbourne und Megan Evans für ihre instruktiven Zeichnungen.

Candida Connolly

Vorwort

Das Anliegen dieses Buches ist es, anspruchsvollen westlichen Musikern nord- und südindische Musik in Liniennotation vorzustellen und ihren Appetit auf mehr anzuregen. Das vorliegende Buch ist keinesfalls eine umfassende Arbeit, für einen westlichen Musiker aber eine gute Möglichkeit, indische Musik auf eine praktische Art und Weise zu erfahren.

Es wurde eine Auswahl von nord- und südindischen Kompositionen getroffen, um die beiden unterschiedlichen Herangehensweisen aufzuzeigen, die von derselben Tradition des Raga und Tala abstammen. Beide Stile haben auf ihre eigene, einzigartige Weise eine ästhetische und kreative Anziehungskraft.

Der indische Raga wird vorgestellt durch improvisierte Melodiephrasen, die *Alapana* (oder *Alap* in der nordindischen Musik) genannt werden, gefolgt von Liedern in einem rhythmischen Rahmen, die einen lyrischen Inhalt mit frommem Charakter aufweisen. Die Melodie wird durch die tonale Bewegung innerhalb eines Ragas erzeugt. Dieser basiert auf den Prinzipien von Konsonanz (oder dem Mischen von Noten), Vibrationen und Obertönen – alles, was einen Klang erzeugt. Die *Gamaka* oder Verzierungskunst der indischen Musik stimmt sowohl bei der hindustanischen als auch bei der karnatischen Musik mit diesen tonalen Werten überein. Das wird durch den Rückhalt eines unterlegten Bordtuns im Hintergrund erreicht.

Die einzelnen Punkte, die in diesem Buch besprochen werden, spiegeln verschiedene Erscheinungsarten und musikalische Formen so wider, dass sie Anfänger ansprechen und ihnen dabei helfen, diese auf ihren jeweiligen Leistungsstand abzustimmen. Obwohl die tonale Bewegung in der indischen Musik für das westliche Ohr ungewohnt sein mag, ist eine Überquerung dieser Trennlinie möglich. Meine Arbeit mit westlichen Musikstudenten sowohl in Europa und Amerika als auch in Indien, aber auch mit indischen Musikstudenten, die solche westlichen Instrumente wie die Violine oder das Saxophon erlernten, hat deren Fähigkeit gezeigt, sowohl das musikalische Ohr als auch die musikalische 'Maschinerie' anzupassen und umzuformen. Um die Wahrnehmung indischer Musik durch das Mischen und Modulieren von Noten zu verstehen, kann das geschriebene Medium zwar helfen, aber den größten Gewinn wird man durch das Hören erzielen. Hierfür wird die Begleit-CD von Nutzen sein.

Ich kann Candidas Arbeit nur wärmstens empfehlen. Sie ist Ausdruck ihrer Hingabe und ihres jahrelangen Studiums der indischen Musik.

Prof. T. V. Gopalakrishnan
Academy of Indian Music and Arts
Chennai

The purpose of this book

In this book I aim to help western musicians understand the Indian approach to melody in order to enable a practical experience of playing Indian music.

While British tastes for curries, Indian fabrics and mysticism have grown over the years our knowledge and appreciation of Indian music has lagged behind. With the popularity of Bollywood and the emergence of Bhangra in the pop scene there is a growth of Indian music in films and advertisements that mixes western styles with Indian. The classical field is the focus of this book.

The first examples show the style of joining notes or embellishments (p. 21, track 2) and exercises in which to practise them (p. 23, track 3). These are followed by elementary songs and studies (p. 26, track 7). This prepares the playing style for the actual compositions, which begin on p. 34 (track 12). The Hindustani section is a brief survey of forms in singing and sitar (p. 50).

With this publication comes an engagement with a rich and ancient culture of beauty and values that both support and enrich those of the west. When playing these songs, imagine India: a hot sunny climate endowed with vivid colours, spices and jewels, beautiful landscapes of all kinds – mountains, deserts, fertile green fields and ocean beaches.

Objectifs de cet ouvrage

Mon propos, par cet ouvrage, est de faciliter l'approche indienne de la mélodie pour les musiciens occidentaux et de leur permettre d'expérimenter la pratique de la musique indienne.

Tandis que le goût occidental pour le *curry*, les tissus indiens et le mysticisme s'est amplifié au cours des années, la connaissance et l'appréciation de la musique indienne sont restées en retrait. La popularité des feuilletons télévisés *Bollywood* et l'émergence du groupe pop **Bhangra** ont accru la présence, dans les films et la publicité, de musique mélangeant les styles indiens et occidentaux. Ce recueil se concentre sur la musique indienne classique.

Les premiers exemples présentent le style utilisé pour relier les notes entre elles et les orner (p. 21, plage 2) et des exercices pour s'y entraîner (p. 23, plage 3), suivis d'airs faciles (p. 26, plage 7), en préparation au style de jeu requis par les compositions proprement dites proposées à partir de la p. 34 (plage 12 du CD). La section *hindoustani* consiste en une brève revue des formes chantées et jouées au sitar (p. 50).

Cet ouvrage s'accompagne de la pénétration d'une culture ancestrale à la beauté foisonnante et de valeurs qui viennent soutenir et enrichir l'Occident. En jouant ces airs, imaginez l'Inde, son climat ensoleillé et chaud, ses couleurs éclatantes, ses épices et ses joyaux, ses paysages magnifiques et variés : montagnes, déserts, champs verdoyants et fertiles, plages bordant l'océan.

Ziel dieses Buches

In diesem Buch möchte ich westlichen Musikern helfen, die indische Herangehensweise an Melodien zu verstehen. Dies möchte ich ihnen durch die praktische Erfahrung des Spielens von indischer Musik ermöglichen.

Während der europäische Geschmack für Curry, indische Stoffe und Mystik über die Jahre zugenommen hat, hinken unser Wissen und unsere Wertschätzung der indischen Musik hinterher. Durch die Popularität Bollywoods und das Auftauchen von Bhangra in der Pop Szene gibt es immer mehr indische Musik in Filmen und der Werbung, die westliche Stilarten mit indischen vermischen. Der klassische Bereich ist das zentrale Thema dieses Buches.

Die ersten Beispiele demonstrieren, wie man Noten aneinander bindet oder verziert (S. 21; CD, Nummer 2) und zeigen Übungen, mit denen man das einüben kann (S. 23; CD, Nummer 3). Danach folgen grundlegende Lieder und Übungen (S. 26; CD, Nummer 7). Danach wird die Spielweise auf die eigentlichen Kompositionen vorbereitet, die auf S. 34 beginnen (CD, Nummer 12). Der hindustanische Abschnitt ist ein kurzer Überblick über die verschiedenen Formen beim Singen und Sitar-Spielen (S. 51).

Dieses Ausgabe bringt die Beschäftigung mit einer reichen und sehr alten Kultur voller Schönheit und Werte mit sich, die jene des Westens sowohl stärken als auch bereichern. Beim Spielen dieser Lieder stelle man sich Indien vor: ein heißes, sonniges Klima, ausgestattet mit kräftigen Farben, Gewürzen und Juwelen, schönen Landschaften und den unterschiedlichsten Bergen, Wüsten, fruchtbaren grünen Feldern und Meeresstränden.

An Introduction to Indian Music

Origins

Indian music has its likely origins in the chanting of the Vedas, a collection of old Indian hymns addressed to ancient Indian deities. This was based on three notes which extended to the seven notes of the octave. There are seven note names which have been used in ancient musical texts and it is the abbreviations of these *Sa Ri Ga Ma Pa Dha Ni* that are used in all Indian music today – folk and film as well as classical music This syllabic notation is termed *sargam* notation and is equivalent to our sol-fa (see page 10).

Raga and Tala

Raga, the melody mould, and Tala, the rhythmic mould, are the two pillars of Indian music. **Ragas** are scalar in movement with individual features brought out by the patterns of improvisation and ornamentation which join notes. Separated notes as in Western playing are sparsely used. The features of a raga are the scale pattern of notes ascending and descending, the sonant and consonant notes, and phrases that highlight the characterisitics of the raga. **Talas** are cyclical with many different time combinations. As well as a language for melody there is also a language for rhythm connected with the ancient classical dance steps. This in turn relates to sounds created on the drum. In music the tala is indicated by hand gestures (see page 58). Rhythmic calculations are also explored through melodic improvisations within the boundaries of the tala cycles.

History: North and South Indian Classical Music

North Indian Classical music or *Hindustani* music is the style played by Ravi Shankar and more widely heard in the West. South Indian classical music or *Karnatic* (also spelt *Carnatic*) is less often heard but, amongst other things, has developed a prominent place for the violin. For this reason this book will begin with South Indian compositions.

Indian classical music bifurcated in the early part of the second millennium under the patronage of the Mughals and the influence of Persian music. The classical music of the North fused the key elements of Persian and Indian practices. It depends heavily on improvisation, the main part of the performance, within a clear structure. Karnatic music meanwhile has a large repertoire of compositions as well as scope in performance for improvisation before and after the composition. The raga concept, the note names and the prominent role of tala all remain common to both styles but the manner of raga presentation, ornamentation and instrumentation differ.

Instruments

Instruments in Indian music are described under four categories: plucked string and bowed, wind and percussion. This goes back to the musical text *Sangitratnakara* of 12th century. The earlier *Natya Sastra* (c.200AD) text also has four categories, but here, along with string and wind, the percussion have two divisions of covered and solid. In North India the main instruments in these categories are the sitar, the shehnai and the tabla; in South India they are the vina, the nagasvaram and the mridangam (a double ended drum); Western instruments have been adapted to Indian music – particularly the violin, mandolin, guitar, saxophone and harmonium. The *tanpura* (*tambura* in the south) or drone instrument holds the pitch for the tonic for the entire concert. It has been used for very long time, although the first sculptural evidence is not found until 9th century AD; it is a distinguishing feature of Indian music. This tonic anchor allows for varied tonal patterns, complex ornamentation and rhythmic calculations, but does not involve modulation to which the western ear is accustomed. Thus the sound that will be created by westerners playing these pieces will initially be plain, but if the gamakas, as mentioned in the preface, are applied the changed sound will be the beginning of a changed ear.

Learning Structure

South India

For South Indian music the learning structure has been laid down for over 400 years. Purandaradasa, considered the grandfather of Karnatic music, responded to the changes affecting Indian music with the influence from the Persian culture of the Mughals. He laid out the first exercises and songs that a student should learn to understand the characteristics of the Karnatic raga and tala.

Examples from this 'syllabus' forms the basis for the Karnatic items in this book. First, examples of scalar exercises (*sarali varisai* and *janta varisai*) and rhythm exercises (*alankara*). These are performed at three speeds with hand gestures to keep the tala, thus a constant pulse is established which controls the speeds of crotchet, quaver and semiquaver. (The speed builds as ability permits.)

Simple songs (*gitams*) are introduced. These are a simple melody sung at one speed from beginning to end. These are followed by rhythmic compositions (*svarajatis*) which are made up of *pallavi* and *charana* as in Chorus and Verse pattern. After this raga studies (*varnams*) are learnt as they show the weaving of the melody line characteristic of the raga, these are played at two, sometimes three speeds. This leads finally to compositions (*kirtanas*). In a *kirtana* there are three musical subjects, the first of which is repeated rather in the manner of a refrain. A concert ends with a dance piece (*tillana*) so this has also been included.

Through this system familiarity with different ragas is gained through learnt material. From here the student begins to make his or her own music through improvisation using the notes of the raga. This occurs as free improvsiation (*alapana*) before the composition and rhythmic improvisation (*kalpana svara*) after the learnt composition as well as improvisation at selected places within the composition.

North India

In North Indian music the learning system has been more varied according to the *Gharana* or singing style (usually named after the province or town in which it is sung) and the guru who took the student into his house to learn as his disciple. This Gurukula-Sishya system of learning also prevailed in the South but there was more uniformity about what was taught. In the North, at the beginning of the last century, an attempt to regularise names and content of ragas was made by the musicologist Pandit Bhatkhande. He also wrote many didactic songs in different ragas to capture the mood of those ragas (*lakshana geet*) – not unlike Purandaradasa.

The Hindustani Raga is elaborated in different styles of improvisation using patterns and structures. These are called *alap*, *jor* and *jhal* for sitar and instrumental playing. *Alap* and *tans* are the improvising styles for vocal singing which also has different styles of composition: *dhupad*, *khyal* and *thumri*.

Aural Tradition

The aural tradition of Indian music means that rarely is the same piece played twice in an identical fashion. This book therefore contains a distillation of pieces that I have learnt in the Karnatic tradition and those that have been selected by the Hindustani teachers at the Bhavan for the Hindustani tradition. This manuscript presentation is, as are all notations used for Indain music, a skeletal reminder giving the framework for individual interpretation of gamaka and melodic variation. Where I have written out gamakas it is only an initial attempt to fill in the melody line with an Indian flavour.

For both systems of Indian music a drum is usually part of the ensemble because the tala is an important aspect of the music. A drone is also a defining characteristic of Indian music.

Indian Violin

The Indian and Western violin is the same instrument but the tuning is different. It is very popular in the South appearing in all Karnatic vocal concerts as an accompanying instrument. It is also established as a solo instrument, owing its popularity to the sustained sound created by the bow and to the similarity it bears to the voice with left hand finger movement. It has recently become more popular in Hindustani music where a larger variety of stringed instruments had previously evolved with the influence of Persian musicians and patrons – such as the sitar, sarod and sarangi.

It was first introduced into the Indian musical world around 1790 by bandsmen of the East India Company in Madras; their fiddlers were often Irish. The fact that one of the earliest Karnatic violinists in the mid-19th century was known as Fiddle Ponnusami attests the likely provenance of this instrument. The younger brother of the eminent composer Muttuswami Dikshitar (1775–1835) Baluswami Dikshitar (1786–1859), went to learn the violin in Madras and then became a court musician in Ettaiyapuram. Over the years the playing style has been modified to suit the more meditative sound quality and fluid left hand manipulation.

Posture

The position for holding the violin is seated cross-legged, with the scroll of the violin resting on the ankle of the right foot. This enables easier left hand finger placement without the problem of holding the violin under the chin as in western technique.

The Tone

Tone quality for Indian music, while needing to be clear, does not require the same degree of projection as in Western music. In the beginning it is mainly the upper two strings (equivalent to A and E) that are used in the playing of melodies. Therefore the bow hold can be more like the folk style, without major attention to the bent thumb and the curved little finger so essential for Western articulation and volume. Currently Indian violinists use a microphone or, increasingly, electric violins for concert performances. While this may arguably distort the original sound, it does allow for a more relaxed approach to the right hand position. The player does not need vibrato.

Tuning

The strings are much looser than on a western violin because the pitch required to accompany vocalists is lower – generally at least a third. This allows the fingers to glide more gently over the strings. The strings are tuned to Lower Doh and Soh, then Doh and Soh, perhaps low F and middle C and F and C above middle C. The tighter strings of western tuning allow the violin to resonate more strongly with greater variation in dynamics and articulation as brought out by bowing technique. The firm application of the left hand in Western technique produces greater volume and vibrato. This is not part of the Indian sound. North Indian violinists sometimes use western tuning, defining it as low Ma, Sa Pa and high Ri, this enables them to reach a wider range of notes and allows for a rounder tone.

Ornamentation

Indian ornamentation requires a very different left hand 'feel' for a full development of Indian style ornamentation, with a looseness and versatility to slide big and small distances to and from the main note. (Some violinists put oil on their fingers to facilitate this.) The need for ornamentation is intrinsic to the Indian sound. For this reason a system of ornamentation marks has been adopted, first introduced by Subbarama Dikshitar (the grandson of the aforementioned violinist, Baluswami Dikshitar) in his Telugu text *Sangita Sampradaya Pradarsini* published in 1904. This notation has been developed by Smt. Vidya Shankar her book *The Art and Science of Carnatic Music* (published 1986 Madras Music Academy) and forms the basis for the signs used here.

For Westerners first approaching this music it is possible to experiment on a western-tuned violin, but it will be harder. The hand slides may feel unnatural to the Western violinist who has learnt to keep the finger securely in one place for sure intonation, but the shake or grace effect is to beautify the raga. Meanwhile intonation is very important and will give the mood and character of the raga. It is underpinned by the drone which plays throughout the performance.

In some places I have suggested fingering to help the beginner approach the Indian concept of joining notes, it is designed to divorce the ear from the eye so that the sound is not stilted by the separate finger placement implied by the western notation. In turn, this sliding will relax the left hand finger pressure.

If it is possible it will help to tune the violin down a tone. The lower strings make a significant difference to the sound quality, creating a more mellow tone. For South Indian tuning this would only be done to the A and E strings – to give strings tuned: G (below middle C), D, G, D. However, in this case the fingers no longer have the same function, at which point it is easier to use *sargam* notation.

Text explanation

○ **Note names**

Sargam notation uses the initial letter or syllable of the 7 Indian note names:

S	Sa	(as in 'far)	Shadja
R	Ri	(as in 'knee')	Rishabha
G	Ga	(as in 'far')	Gandhara
M	Ma	(as in 'far')	Madhyama
P	Pa	(as in 'far')	Panchama
D	Dha	(as in 'far')	Dhaivata
N	Ni	(as in 'knee')	Nishadha

In the sargam notation following I have indicated note length thus:

Sa = crotchet
sa = quaver
s = semiquaver

Rests are defined by punctuation marks,

; = crotchet rest
, = quaver rest
. = semiquaver rest

A dot above the note refers to the higher octave and likewise a dot below to the lower.

○ **South Indian sargam terminology**

Where numbers appear under these they refer to the flattened or sharpened position of the note. This gives the enharmonic tuning that a western violinist would recognise for example between E and F♭. The position of the note in relation to Sa is particularly significant when placed against a drone.

Where Sa = D	Ri_1 = E♭	Ga_1 = F♭	Ma_1 = G
	Ri_2 = E	Ga_2 = F	Ma_2 = G♯
	Ri_3 = E♯	Ga_3 = F♯	

and Pa = A	Dha_1 = B♭	Ni_1 = C♭,
	Dha_2 = B,	Ni_2 = C,
	Dha_3 = B♯	Ni_3 = C♯

○ **Karnatic Rhythm**

The correct counting system is made up of blocks of counting structures. The preliminary three are :

1. the *Anudrutam* = one beat;
2. the *Drutam* = beat and a wave;
3. the *Laghu* = beat and finger count beginning with the little finger, this can be varying in number.

In this book there are talas with 2 and 3 finger counts.

Adi Tala: 4 + 2 +2 =   1   2   3   4   5   6   7   8   (See pages 58 and 59)
beat, little finger, ring finger, middle finger, beat, wave, beat , wave.

Rupaka tala: 2+ 4 =   1   2   3   4   5   6
beat, wave, beat, little finger, ring finger, middle finger.

Misra Chapu: 3 + 2 + 2 = 1   2   3   4   5   6   7
wave, little finger, ring finger   beat, wave, beat, wave.

○ **Hindustani Rhythm**

Three Talas are used in this book:

Tin Tal = 16 beats

The counting system for Tin Tal or 16 beats can be held on the cracks of the four fingers beginning with the little finger. However, the common pattern is to hold the beat on every 4th beat with a clap on the 1st, 5th and 13th beat and a wave on the 9th beat:

x				x				0				x			
1	2	3	4	5	6	7	8	9	10	11	12	13	14	15	16
clap,	2	3	4,	clap,	2	3	4	wave,	2	3	4	clap,	2	3	4

Rupak Tal = 7 beats
here mean 7 counts: like the Karnatic Misra Chapu

Deepchandi Tal = 14 beats

0			x		x		0		x		x	
1	2	3	4	5	6	7	8	9	10	11	12	13	14

Improvisation passages usually include and end with a Tihai which is a thrice repeated pattern.

○ **North Indian sargam terminology**

Where notes are underlined they are flattened from the natural or major scale position where an accent appears above (only for Ma) the note is sharpened. Note also that Ri is sung as Re (as in 'neigh').

Where Sa = D	Re = E♭,	Ga = F,	Ma = G
	Re = E	Ga = F♯	Má = G♯
Pa= A	Dha =B♭	Ni = C	
	Dha = B	Ni = C♯	

Both North and South Indian music is sung using sargam to develop the tonal world of the raga and the rhythmic accuracy of phrasing. It is also sung using syllables such as *'ta da na'*.

The *arohana* (ascending pattern) and *avarohana* (descending pattern) is given at the beginning of each raga composition, with reference to this sargam terminology. These notes are used to elaborate the raga in improvisation before beginning the composition.

Some lyrics are given under the notes because Indian music stems from the vocal tradition. Instruments imitate the voice as closely as possible.

○ **Rhythm**

The time cycle for each composition is indicated by hand gestures while singing or by the audience while the artists are playing! This means irregular bar counts will be made clear by the hand gestures. I have applied Western time signatures for ease of reading.

Glossary

A glossary at the end of the book explains Indian terms used.

Karnatic Music

In Karnatic music the composition has a prominent role in the raga presentation. There are various forms, some contained in this book. Each composition captures the mood and flavour of the raga. I acknowledge the help I have received both from the Bhavan teachers and Professor T. V. Gopalakrishanan in this summary.

Ragas in Karnatic music

The Raga is a series of notes which determines the melody line. There are hundreds of different ragas in both North and South Indian music, some of which are very old and some which have been created recently. They are grouped into raga families.

In South India there is a raga classification system which reached its final form in the 18th century by Govindacharya. It covers all the possible combinations of tone, semi-tone and augmented tone in each tetrachord of the octave with a perfect fifth (Doh Soh) using the same 7 notes in ascent and descent. These are called the 72 *melakarta* (lit. 'king of the court').

Under these so-called *janaka* or 'parent scales' are collected all the *janya* or 'child' ragas: that is ragas which are variations on the linear sequence of notes in the 'parent mela'. There are 3 main types of *janya* ragas:

> *Asampurna* = incomplete ragas using less or more than seven notes in ascent or descent as in Malahari raga in the first two songs (pp. 26, 28)
> *Vakra* = ragas using a 'zig-zag' path of ascent or decent as in the Suposhini Raga. (p. 41)
> *Bhashanga* = ragas with a 'foreign' note interjected at rare but well defined moments.

Often the *janya* raga is older than the classifying raga so there is no sense of derivation of the *janya* from the *janaka*, so 'parent' is a rather misleading term. Some ragas have more than seven notes for example Bhairavi in Hindustani music uses all twelve notes, though not consecutively as in the chromatic scale, and different ragas also use different variants of the same note, for example in Karnatic music **Varali** (D E♭ F♭ G♯ A Bb C♯ D) uses a sharper 4th note, Ma or G♯ than in **Kalyani** (D E F♯ G♯ A B C♯ D).

Whilst association of time and season is relevant to some ragas this is far more prominent in the Hindustani tradition. 'Bhava' or mood is a key part of the raga performance in Karnatic music and reflects the meaning of the texts which are about the search of the soul for God. Bhava is also important in Hindustani music.

Compositions

There are ragas with hundreds of compositions and ragas with just one. While compositions from Purandaradasa in the 16th century are part of the Karnatic tradition it was in the 18th and 19th century that the Trinity of Karnatic composers, Tyagaraja, Dikshitar and Syama Sastri, established the core repertoire of what we understand as Karnatic music. Many compositions have been added to this repertoire, the lyrics being in Sanskrit, the classical language of India, and also in Telugu and Tamil, two vernacular tongues of the South. Three of Tyagaraja's composition are included in this book.

The improvisation that takes place before, after and at places within the composition is beyond the scope of this book.

Ornaments or Gamakas

Gamakas are an integral part of the scale in Karnatic music rather than an additional feature. What happens between the notes is as important as the bare notes themselves.

For the sake of this introductory work I have applied signs as in the baroque manner of ornamentation of notes. However, in the first two kirtana I have written the gamakas out approximately in western notation This is to help generate the beginnings of an 'Indian sound' to what would otherwise be a western rendition of a modal tune. There are several versions of gamakas and approaches to Indian ornamentation – such as those propounded by Prof. Sambamoorthy. Very few teachers refer to them by name and different musicians have their own individual interpretation of them.

To quote the 3rd century AD authority Bharata in his *Natya Sastra*:

> *'A raga without subtle ornamented features is like a moonless night, a creeper without flowers, a river without water, a woman without jewellery'*

Some attempt at ornamentation, therefore, is part and parcel of engaging with Indian music. However, in the notation of Indian music there is rarely any reference to the gamakas; commonly they are learnt by ear from the teacher. The notation for an Indian composition comes in sargam with the addition of commas to lengthen notes or notes underlined to make them faster (see p. 10). There is a tala (time cycle) into which the main notes fit. This serves as a skeletal reminder of the melody.

In this written attempt to make the music accessible to western musicians compromises over exact delineation of ornament will be inevitable. The reader will be encouraged to find a satisfying answer in hearing live concerts by great Indian musicians, or indeed finding an Indian music teacher himself.

Traditionally students are taught the **Mayamalavagaula** raga first. This has a suitable pattern for finger position for the first finger exercises: the notes come in semitonal pairs: SaRi GaMa PaDha NiSa and are separated by an augmented tone on each string. This is the parent raga for **Malahari** in which the first songs are set, (an *asampurna janya* raga using five notes in ascent and six notes in descent – D E♭ G A B♭D D B♭ A G F♯ E♭ D). This choice of raga could have been made because Purandaradasa was a vina player as these intervals are easier to play than to sing.

Introduction à la musique indienne

Les origines

Les racines les plus probables de la musique indienne sont constituées par la psalmodie des *vedas* de l'hymnologie hindoue. Celle-ci s'organisait autour de trois notes et pouvait s'étendre aux sept notes de l'octave. Sept noms de notes apparaissent dans les textes musicaux anciens et ce sont leurs abréviations, *Sa Ri Ga Ma Pa Dha Ni*, qui sont aujourd'hui utilisées dans toute la musique indienne (traditionnelle, classique ou musique de film). Cette notation syllabique, équivalent de notre notation solfégique, s'appelle la notation *sargam* (voir p. 14).

Raga et Tala

Le *raga*, cadre mélodique, et le *tala*, cadre rythmique, constituent les deux piliers de la musique indienne. Les *ragas* consistent en mouvements de gammes auxquels s'ajoutent des traits singuliers apportés par les formules d'improvisation et d'ornementation qui relient les notes. Les intervalles disjoints entre les notes, fréquents dans la musique occidentale, sont peu utilisés. Un *raga* comprend une formule de gamme ascendante et descendante, des notes sonnantes et consonantes et des phrases qui mettent en valeur ses caractéristiques. Les *talas* sont cycliques et présentent de multiples combinaisons de mesures. De même qu'il existe un langage de la mélodie, il existe un langage du rythme attaché aux anciens pas de danse classique. Ceux-ci sont eux-mêmes liés aux sons produits par le tambour. Dans la musique, le *tala* est indiqué par des gestes manuels (voir p. 58). Divers agencements rythmiques sont également exploités par les improvisations mélodiques progressant à l'intérieur du cadre cyclique des *talas*.

Histoire : musique classique du nord et du sud de l'Inde

La musique classique de l'Inde du Nord ou musique *hindoustanaise*, style pratiqué par Ravi Shankar, est la plus répandue en occident. La musique classique du sud de l'Inde ou musique *carnatique*, moins connue, a, de son côté, réservé une place dominante au violon. C'est la raison pour laquelle cet ouvrage s'intéresse d'abord aux compositions de l'Inde méridionale.

La musique classique indienne se divisa en deux courants au début du deuxième millénaire sous la domination des Moghols et l'influence de la musique perse. La musique classique hindoustanaise des régions du nord, associant les principaux éléments des pratiques perse et indienne, repose fortement sur l'improvisation, principale constituante de l'exécution à l'intérieur d'une structure claire, tandis que la musique carnatique des régions du sud dispose d'un ample répertoire de compositions et d'un espace réservé à l'improvisation avant et après l'exécution des pièces composées. Le concept de *raga*, les noms des notes et le rôle primordial du *tala* demeurent communs aux deux styles mais la manière de présenter le *raga*, l'ornementation et l'instrumentation diffèrent de l'un à l'autre.

Les instruments

Les instruments de musique indiens se classent en quatre catégories définies par le texte sur la musique du *Sangitratnakara* du XIIe siècle : cordes pincées, cordes frottées, instruments à vent et instruments à percussion. Le *Natya Sastra*, plus ancien (environ 200 avant J.C.), indique également quatre sortes d'instruments mais en plus des cordes et des instruments à vent, les instruments à percussion sont subdivisés en instruments recouverts et instruments solides. Les principaux instruments pratiqués au nord de l'Inde sont le **sitar**, le **shehnai** et le **tabla**, ceux représentés dans le sud de l'Inde, le **vina**, le **nagasvaram** et le **mridangam** (tambour à deux surfaces opposées). Certains instruments, comme le violon, la mandoline, la guitare, le saxophone et l'harmonium, ont été adaptés à la musique indienne (1). Le **tanpura** (**tambura** dans le sud), instrument interprétant le bourdon, joue la tonique pendant tout le concert.

Instrument distinctif de la musique indienne, on l'a utilisé de tous temps, bien que la première sculpture le représentant ne date que du IXe siècle. Cet ancrage à la tonique permet des formules tonales variées, une ornementation complexe et une rythmique élaborée mais exclut la modulation à laquelle est habituée l'oreille occidentale. Ceci explique que, dans un premier temps, les sons produits par des occidentaux jouant ces pièces se révèleront plats, mais en appliquant les gamakas, mentionnés dans la préface, la transformation progressive de la sonorité témoignera de la mutation de l'oreille.

Plan d'étude

Sud de l'Inde

Les règles d'apprentissage de la musique du sud de l'Inde ont été établies depuis plus de 400 ans par **Purandaradasa**, considéré comme le père de la musique carnatique, qui répercuta les changements qui affectèrent la musique indienne sous l'influence de la culture perse des Moghols. Il élabora les premiers exercices et chants à étudier pour intégrer les principes du *raga* et du *tala* carnatiques.

Des exemples de ce « programme » forment la base de la partie carnatique de ce volume dont les premiers exercices de gammes (*sarali varisai* et *janta varisai*) et exercices rythmiques (*alankara*) seront joués selon trois tempos. Les gestes manuels suivent le *tala* de façon à maintenir une pulsation constante qui détermine la vitesse des noires, des croches et des doubles croches. (La vitesse croît en fonction des capacités de chacun.)

Le recueil débute par des chants simples (*gitams*), mélodies dénuées de complexité et chantées sur un seul tempo du début à la fin. Ceux-ci sont suivis de compositions rythmiques (*svarajatis*) constituées de *pallavi* et de *charana*, dont la structure alterne chœur et verset. Ensuite, des études (*varnams*), que l'on jouera à deux et parfois trois vitesses différentes, tracent la conduite caractéristique de la ligne mélodique du *raga*, avant d'aborder, finalement, les compositions (*kirtanas*) qui comportent trois sujets musicaux dont le premier est répété un peu à la manière d'un refrain. Une danse (*tillana*), qui clôt traditionnellement le concert, y a également été incluse.

Par cette méthode et au fil des différents morceaux étudiés, on se familiarisera avec différents ragas. A partir de là, l'étudiant commencera à improviser sa propre musique en utilisant les notes du raga. L'improvisation est libre (*alapana*) lorsqu'elle précède la composition étudiée et rythmique (*kalpana svara*) si elle la suit et à certains endroits spécifiques de la composition.

Nord de l'Inde

La méthode d'apprentissage de la musique du nord de l'Inde variait davantage selon le *gharana* ou style chanté, généralement désigné par le nom de la province ou de la ville dont il provient, et le gourou qui accueillait l'étudiant chez lui pour en faire son disciple. Cet enseignement *gurukula-sishya* avait également cours dans le Sud mais y était plus uniformisé. Au début du siècle dernier, le musicologue **Pandit Bhatkande** entreprit de recenser les noms et le contenu des ragas des régions du nord de l'Inde. Il écrivit aussi de nombreux chants didactiques restituant l'atmosphère propre aux différents ragas – un peu à la manière de Purandaradasa.

Le raga hindoustanais se développe selon plusieurs styles d'improvisation faisant appel à des formules et à des structures diverses appelées *alap*, *jor*, et *jhal* pour le sitar et le jeu instrumental. *Alap* et *tans* sont des styles d'improvisation chantée. *dhrupad*, *khyal* et *thumri* sont différents styles de chants.

Tradition orale

La tradition orale et auditive de la musique indienne signifie

---

(1) pour plus de renseignements, voir l'affiche Indian Musical Instruments *éditée par le Centre Bharatiay Vidya Bhavan (Londres)*

qu'une même pièce est rarement jouée deux fois de la même façon. Ce recueil contient donc une sélection de pièces que j'ai apprises dans la tradition carnatique et de pièces choisies par les professeurs hindoustanais du centre Bhavan illustrant la tradition du nord de L'Inde. Leur transcription manuscrite, comme toute notation de musique indienne, est un rappel de l'ossature du cadre offert à l'interprétation personnelle des gamakas et des variations mélodiques. Aux endroits où j'ai noté des *gamakas*, ceux-ci ne représentent qu'une tentative de coloration indienne de la ligne mélodique.

Dans les deux traditions de musique indienne, un tambour fait généralement partie de l'ensemble instrumental. Le *tala* ainsi que le bourdon sont des aspects typiques fondamentaux de toute la musique indienne.

Le violon indien

Le violon indien et le violon occidental sont des instruments identiques mais accordés différemment. Le violon est très populaire dans le sud de l'Inde où il accompagne tous les concerts vocaux carnatiques. Il est également bien établi comme instrument soliste, apprécié pour le son soutenu créé par l'archet et sa similarité avec la voix produite par le mouvement des doigts de la main gauche. Il a récemment gagné du terrain dans la musique hindoustanaise qui avait jadis, sous l'influence des musiciens et des mécènes perses, développé un plus large éventail d'instruments à cordes, tels que le **sitar**, le **sarod** et le **sarangi**.

Le violon fut introduit dans l'univers musical indien à Madras, vers 1790, par des musiciens de l'East India Company. Ces violonistes traditionnels (*fiddlers*) étaient souvent irlandais. Que l'un des premiers violonistes carnatiques, au milieu du XIXe siècle, fût connu sous le nom de Fiddle Ponnusami atteste la provenance probable de cet instrument. Le plus jeune frère du grand compositeur Muttusvami Dikshitar (1775 – 1835), Balusvami Dikshitar (1786-1859) se rendit à Madras pour y apprendre le violon et devint musicien de la cour d'Ettaiyapuram. Au fil des années, le jeu violonistique s'est orienté vers une qualité de son de caractère plutôt méditatif et vers une technique de main gauche plus fluide.

Position
On tient le violon en position assise, jambes croisées, la volute du violon reposant sur la cheville droite. Cette position permet un meilleur placement des doigts de la main gauche tout en écartant la difficulté de tenue du violon sous le menton selon la technique occidentale.

Son
La qualité sonore de la musique indienne, tout en nécessitant une grande clarté, n'exige pas le même niveau de projection que la musique occidentale. Dans un premier temps, ce sont principalement les deux cordes supérieures (équivalentes aux cordes de *la* et de *mi*) qui sont utilisées pour interpréter les mélodies. La tenue de l'archet peut donc plus s'apparenter au style traditionnel, sans attention particulière à la courbure du pouce et du petit doigt si essentielle à l'articulation et au volume de la technique occidentale. Les violonistes indiens actuels se servent d'un microphone ou, de plus en plus, de violons amplifiés pour les concerts publics. Bien que cette pratique contestable puisse déformer la sonorité originale, elle permet une approche plus détendue de la position de la main droite et évite la pratique du vibrato.

Accord
Les cordes du violon indien sont beaucoup plus relâchées que celles d'un violon occidental car la hauteur de son nécessaire à l'accompagnement des vocalistes est plus grave en Inde qu'en Occident – en général d'au moins une tierce – laissant les doigts glisser plus doucement sur elles. L'accord des cordes est *ut* grave et *sol*, puis *ut* et *sol*, ou peut-être *fa* grave et *ut* médium, *fa* et *ut* au-dessus de *ut* médium. Les cordes plus tendues du violon occidental le font résonner plus fort et permettent une grande diversité de nuances et de phrasé grâce à la technique de l'archet. Le volume sonore ample dû à la pression ferme de la main gauche de la technique occidentale et le vibrato sont étrangers à la sonorité indienne. Les violonistes du nord de l'Inde utilisent parfois l'accord occidental, qu'ils définissent comme *Ma* grave, *Sa*, *Pa* et *Ri* aigu, afin d'atteindre un plus grand ambitus et d'obtenir un son plus rond.

Ornementation
Pour s'épanouir totalement, l'ornementation indienne demande un « sensibilité » très particulière de la main gauche, une souplesse et une habileté à glisser sur des grandes et des petites distances depuis et vers la note principale. (Certains violonistes enduisent leurs doigts d'huile pour faciliter ces mouvements.) L'ornementation faisant partie intrinsèque de la sonorité indienne, un ensemble de signes d'ornements a été codifié. Celui-ci fut élaboré par Subbarama Dikshitar (petit-fils du violoniste mentionné plus haut, Baluswani Dikshitar) dans son recueil telgu *Sangita Sqmpradaya Pradarsini* publié en 1904. Cette notation a été développée par Smt. Vidya Shankar dans son ouvrage *The Art and Science of Carnatic Music* (Madras Music Academy, 1968) et constitue la base des signes utilisés ici.

Les Occidentaux qui abordent pour la première fois cette musique peuvent le faire sur un violon accordé à l'occidentale mais la tâche leur sera plus difficile. Les glissements de la main peuvent paraître anti-naturels au violoniste occidental habitué à maintenir fermement le doigt sur un point précis pour une intonation sûre. Les effets de tremblements et d'ornements ont néanmoins pour but d'embellir le *raga*, tandis que l'intonation est essentielle à sa caractérisation et à son climat. Le bourdon soutien son exécution d'un bout à l'autre.

A certains endroits, j'ai proposé des doigtés glissés qui aideront le débutant à se familiariser avec le concept indien de notes jointes. Ceux-ci sont conçus pour dissocier l'oreille et l'œil de façon à ne pas produire les sons séparés déterminés par les différentes positions occidentales des doigts. Par ailleurs, ce glissement détendra la pression des doigts de la main gauche.

Dans la mesure du possible, il sera préférable de baisser l'accord du violon d'un ton. Les cordes graves apportent une différence de qualité significative à la sonorité en l'adoucissant. Pour la musique de l'Inde méridionale, on n'abaissera que les cordes de *la* et de *mi* pour obtenir l'accord *sol* (sous *ut* médium), *ré*, *sol*, *ré*. Dans ce cas, les doigts ne remplissent pas la même fonction, l'utilisation de la notation *sargam* se trouvera facilitée.

Principes théoriques

○ **Nom des notes**

La notation *sargam* utilise les premières lettres ou syllabes des 7 noms de notes indiens :

S	Sa	Shadja
R	Ri	Rishabha
G	Ga	Gandhara
M	Ma	Madhyama
P	Pa	Panchama
D	Dha	Dhaivata
N	Ni	Nishadha

Dans la notation *sargam*, j'ai indiqué les durées des notes comme suit :

Sa = noire
sa = croche
s = double croche

Les silences sont exprimés par les signes de ponctuation suivants :

; = soupir
, = demi-soupir
. = quart de soupir

Un point placé au-dessus de la note indique l'octave supérieure, un point placé en dessous de la note indique l'octave inférieure.

○ **Terminologie *sargam* du sud de l'Inde**

Les nombres accompagnant le nom d'une note se rattachent à l'abaissement (bémol) ou le haussement (dièse) de cette note et indiquent les distinctions enharmoniques qu'un violoniste occidental reconnaît, par exemple, entre *mi* et *fa* bémol. La position de la note par rapport à *Sa* est particulièrement révélatrice quand elle est accompagnée d'un bourdon.

Lorsque Sa = ré

$Ri_1 = mi\flat$	$Ga_1 = fa\flat$	$Ma_1 = sol$
$Ri_2 = mi$	$Ga_2 = fa$	$Ma_2 = sol\sharp$
$Ri_3 = mi\sharp$	$Ga_3 = fa\sharp$	

Et Pa = la

$Dha_1 = si\flat$	$Ni_1 = do\flat$,
$Dha_2 = si$,	$Ni_2 = do$,
$Dha_3 = si\sharp$	$Ni_3 = do\sharp$

○ **Terminologie *sargam* du nord de l'Inde**

Les notes soulignées sont abaissées de leur hauteur naturelle ou de leur position dans la gamme majeure. Les notes surmontées d'un point (seulement pour Ma) sont haussées. Ri est chanté en prononçant Ré.

Lorsque Sa = ré

Re = mi$\flat$	Ga = fa,	Ma = sol
Re = mi	Ga = fa$\sharp$	Mà = so$\sharp$

Et Pa = la

Dha = si$\flat$	Ni = do
Dha = si	Ni = do$\sharp$

La musique du nord et du sud de l'Inde est chantée en utilisant le *sargam* pour enrichir l'univers tonal du raga et la précision rythmique du phrasé. On chante également sur des onomatopées telles que « ta *da na* ».

L'*arohana* (configuration ascendante) et l'*avarohana* (configuration descendante) sont donnés au début de chaque composition raga avec la référence de sa terminologie *sargam*. Ces notes servent à élaborer le raga en improvisant avant de jouer la composition. Quelques paroles apparaissent sous les notes, rappelant l'enracinement de la musique indienne dans la tradition vocale. Les instrumentistes s'efforcent le plus possible d'imiter la voix.

○ **Rythme**

Le cycle de mesure de chaque composition est indiqué par une gestuelle manuelle tout en chantant ou imposé par le public pendant que les artistes jouent ! Les mesures irrégulières sont ainsi explicitées par les gestes de la main. J'ai ajouté des indications de mesure occidentales pour faciliter la lecture.

○ **Rythme carnatique**

Le système exact de battue est décomposé en blocs de structures de comptage dont les trois premières sont :
1. l'*anadrutam* = 1 battement
2. le *drutam* = 1 battement et signe de la main
3. le *laghu* = 1 battement et battue sur les doigts, commençant par l'auriculaire, dont le nombre d'unités peut varier
Ce recueil contient des talas de 2 et 3 unités de battue sur les doigts.

	x				x		x	
adi tala : 4 + 2 + 2 =	1	2	3	4	5	6	7	8
	temps,	auricul.,	annul.,	médium,	temps,	signe/main,	temps,	signe (voir p. 58 et 59)

rupaka tala : 2 + 4 =	1	2	3	4	5	6
	temps,	signe/main,	temps,	annul.,	auricul.,	médium

misra chapu : 3 + 2 + 2 =	1	2	3	4	5	6	7
	signe/main,	auricul.,	annul.,	temps,	signe/main,	temps,	signe/main

Rythme hindoustanais

Trois talas figurent dans ce recueil :

tin tal = 16 pulsations

La battue de *tin tal* ou de 6 pulsations peut se faire sur les articulations de doigts en commençant par l'auriculaire. Cependant, la formule courante consiste à interrompre la pulsation tous les 4 temps, à frapper dans les mains le 1er , le 5ème et le 13ème temps et à marquer d'un signe de la main le 9ème temps.

x				x				0				x			
1	2	3	4	5	6	7	8	9	10	11	12	13	14	15	16
clap,	2	3	4,	clap,	2	3	4	signe	2	3	4	clap,	2	3	4

rupak tal = 7 pulsations
même battue que le *misra chapu* carnatique   *deepchandi* tal = 14 pulsations

0			x		x		0			x		x	
1	2	3	4	5	6	7	8	9	10	11	12	13	14

Glossaire

Un glossaire placé à la fin du volume explique les termes indiens employés.

Les improvisations, en général, comportent et se terminent par un *tihai* qui est une formule répétée trois fois.

La musique carnatique

La composition tient un rôle primordial dans la progression du raga de la musique carnatique. Il en existe des formes diverses dont certaines sont représentées dans ce recueil. Chaque composition reflète le climat et le caractère du raga. Je remercie les professeurs du Centre Bhavan et le professeur T.V. Gopalakrishnan de leur participation à la rédaction de ce résumé.

Les ragas dans la musique carnatique

Le raga est une série de notes qui détermine la ligne mélodique. Il en existe des centaines dans la musique du nord et du sud de l'Inde. Certains sont très anciens, d'autres sont de création récente. Ils sont regroupés en familles.

Dans le **sud de l'Inde**, le système de classification des ragas atteignit sa forme définitive au XVIIIe siècle grâce à Govindarcharya. Il recouvre toutes les combinaisons possibles de ton, demi-ton et ton augmenté à l'intérieur de chaque tétracorde de l'octave délimité par une quinte juste et utilisant les sept mêmes notes en ordre ascendant et descendant. Ces combinaisons sont appelées les *72 melakarta* (littéralement « roi dans sa cour »).

Sous le nom de *janaka* sont regroupés tous les *janya* ou ragas « fils » à savoir ragas dérivés de la séquence linéaire de notes du *mela* « père ». Il existe trois types principaux de ragas *janya* :

> *asampurna* = « pas sept » notes : raga employant moins ou plus de sept notes en ordre ascendant ou descendant, comme dans le raga Malahari des deux premiers chants (p. 26, 28).
> *vakra* = raga cheminant en zig-zag ascendant ou descendant, comme dans le raga Suposhini (p. 41).
> *bhashanga* = raga dans lesquels est introduite une note « étrangère » à quelques endroits rares mais précis.

Il arrive souvent que le raga *janya* soit plus ancien que le raga classifié et que la dérivation du *janya* à partir du *janaka* n'existe pas, le terme de « père » est donc assez trompeur. Certains ragas possèdent plus de sept notes : le raga Bhairavi de la musique hindoustanais, par exemple, utilise les douze notes mais pas consécutivement de façon chromatique. Il arrive que des ragas distincts utilisent des variantes de la même note, par exemple le raga **Varali** de la musique carnatique (*ré, mi♭, fa♭, sol♯, la, si♭, do♯, ré*) emploie un quatrième degré plus élevé, Ma ou *sol* dièse, que le raga **Kalyani** (*ré, mi, fa♯, sol♯, la, si, do♯, ré*).

Tandis que l'association avec le temps qu'il fait et la saison, caractéristique de certains ragas, est beaucoup plus présente dans la tradition hindoustanaise, le « *bhava* », ou installation de l'atmosphère du raga, constitue une part essentielle de l'interprétation du raga de la musique carnatique. Il reflète le sens des textes orientés vers la recherche de Dieu par l'âme. Le *bhava* est également important dans la musique hindoustanaise.

Compositions

Certains ragas sont sources de centaines de compositions et d'autres d'une seule. Les compositions de **Purandaradasa** du XVIe siècle appartiennent déjà à la tradition carnatique, mais c'est au cours des XVIIIe et XIXe siècles que le trio des compositeurs carnatiques **Tyagaraja**, **Dikshitar** et **Syama Sastri** établit le répertoire de fonds de ce que l'on définit comme la musique carnatique. Ce répertoire s'est enrichi de nombreuses compositions dont les textes sont rédigés en sanscrit, langue classique de l'Inde, ainsi qu'en telugu et en tamoul, deux langues vernaculaires des régions sud. Trois compositions de Tyagaraja figurent dans ce recueil. L'improvisation qui les précède, les suit et s'y intercale dépasse les limites de ce volume.

Ornements ou *gamakas*

Les *gamakas* sont considérés comme partie intégrante des échelles de la musique carnatique et non comme des traits ajoutés. Ce qui se passe entre les notes est aussi important que les notes elles-mêmes.

Dans l'esprit de cette initiation, j'ai introduit des signes sur le modèle baroque d'ornementation des notes. J'ai, de même, transcrit de manière approchée les deux premiers *kirtana* selon la notation occidentale de façon à aider les débuts de la production d'une « sonorité indienne » et éviter l'écueil de l'exécution occidentale d'une mélodie modale. Il existe plusieurs versions des gamakas et plusieurs approches de l'art de l'ornementation indienne – à l'image de celle proposée par le Pr Sambamoorthy. Très peu de maîtres attribuent un nom aux gamakas qu'ils exécutent et chaque musicien en possède sa propre interprétation.

Citons le maître **Bharata**, au IIIe siècle dans son *Natya Sastra* :

> *Un raga sans traits ornementaux subtils est comme une nuit sans lune, une plante grimpante sans fleurs, une rivière sans eau, une femme sans bijoux.*

La démarche d'ornementation représente donc un des principes de l'apprentissage de la musique indienne. Toutefois, les références aux gamakas sont rares dans l'écriture. Ceux-ci sont généralement appris à l'oreille auprès d'un professeur. La notation d'une composition indienne emprunte le système *sargam* auquel s'ajoutent des virgules pour signifier l'allongement de la durée des notes ou des soulignements pour signifier leur mouvement plus rapide (voir p. 14). Les notes principales entrent dans un *tala* (cycle mesuré) et servent d'ossature à la mélodie.

Notre tentative de transcription destinée à rendre cette musique accessible aux musiciens occidentaux ne peut éviter l'approximation quant aux contours exacts des ornements et ne saurait donc remplacer la fréquentation de concerts donnés par de grands musiciens indiens et, surtout, l'enseignement d'un maître de musique indienne.

L'apprentissage commence traditionnellement par le raga Mayamalavagaula qui offre une formule adaptée à la position des premiers exercices des doigts : les notes y apparaissent groupées par deux, à intervalle de demi-tons séparés d'une seconde augmentées sur chaque corde : SaRi GaMa PaDha NiSa. Il s'agit du raga-père du raga **malahari** des premiers chants (raga *asampurna janya* sur cinq notes ascendantes et six notes descendantes – *ré, mi♭, sol, la, si♭, ré, ré, si♭, la, sol, fa♯, mi♭, ré*). Ce choix de raga a peut-être été dicté par le fait que Purandaradasa jouait du vina et que ces intervalles sont plus faciles à exécuter sur un instrument qu'à chanter.

Eine Einführung in die indische Musik

Ursprünge

Die indische Musik hat ihre Ursprünge wahrscheinlich in der Rezitation der Rigveda, der altindischen Hymnensammlung. Sie gründete sich auf drei Noten, die auf die sieben Noten der Oktave erweitert wurden. Es gibt sieben Notennamen, die in alten Musiktexten benutzt wurden und es sind deren Abkürzungen *Sa Ri Ga Ma Pa Dha Ni*, die heutzutage in der gesamten indischen Musik verwendet werden – in der Volksmusik und dem Film ebenso wie in der klassischen Musik. Diese syllabische Notation wird *Sargam*-Notation genannt und ist mit unserer Tonika-Do-Methode gleichzusetzen (s. S. 18).

Raga und Tala

Raga, die melodische, und Tala, die rhythmische Gestalt, sind die beiden Säulen der indischen Musik. **Ragas** sind von der Bewegung her tonleiterartig mit individuellen Merkmalen, die durch die Improvisations- und Verzierungsmuster, die die Noten miteinander verbinden, herausgearbeitet werden. Einzelnoten, wie sie beim westlichen Musizieren vorkommen, werden nur sehr spärlich verwendet. Die Merkmale eines Raga sind die Tonleiterschemata mit ihren auf- und absteigenden Noten, die klingenden und anklingenden Noten, sowie Wendungen, die die Charakteristika eines Raga hervorheben. **Talas** sind Perioden mit vielen unterschiedlichen Zeitkombinationen. Es gibt sowohl eine Sprache für Melodien als auch eine für den Rhythmus, die mit den alten klassischen Tanzschritten verbunden ist. Dies bezieht sich wiederum auf Klänge, die auf der Trommel erzeugt werden. In der Musik wird der Tala durch Handzeichen angegeben (s. S. 58).

Geschichte: nord- und südindische klassische Musik

Der Stil, den Ravi Shankar spielt und der im Westen eher bekannt ist, ist die nordindische klassische oder *hindustanische* Musik. Von der südindischen klassischen oder *karnatischen* Musik (auch *carnatisch* buchstabiert) hört man seltener, aber gerade diese hat, neben anderen Dingen, der Violine einen herausragenden Platz zugewiesen. Aus diesem Grund beginnt dieses Buch mit südindischen Kompositionen.

Die klassische indische Musik spaltete sich zu Beginn des zweiten Jahrtausends unter der Schirmherrschaft der Mughals und dem Einfluss von persischer Musik. Die klassische Musik des Nordens verschmolz die Schlüsselelemente von persischen und indischen Gepflogenheiten. Sie ist sehr stark auf die Improvisation angewiesen, wobei der Hauptteil des Vortrags innerhalb einer festgelegten Reihenfolge abläuft. Dagegen hat die karnatische Musik nicht nur ein weitreichendes Repertoire an Kompositionen, sondern auch während des Vortrags Raum für Improvisationen vor und nach der Komposition. Das Konzept des Raga, die Notennamen und die auffallend wichtige Rolle des Tala bleiben beiden Stilen gemein, aber die Art, wie der Raga präsentiert wird, die Verzierungskunst und die Instrumentation sind unterschiedlich.

Instrumente

In der indischen Musik werden die Instrumente in vier Kategorien eingeteilt: gezupfte und gestrichene Saiten-instrumente, Blas- und Schlaginstrumente. Diese Einteilung geht auf den Musiktraktat *Sangita-Ratnakara* aus dem 12. Jahrhundert zurück. Der früher entstandene Text *Natya-Sastra* (um 200 n. Chr.) hat ebenfalls vier Kategorien, aber hier werden neben Saiten- und Blasinstrumenten die Schlaginstrumente in Trommeln und Idiophone unterteilt. In Nordindien sind die Hauptinstrumente in diesen Kategorien die Sitar, die Shehnai und die Tabla; in Südindien sind es die Vina, der Nagasvaram und der Mridangam (eine zweiseitige Trommel); auch westliche Instrumente wurden in die indische Musik übernommen – besonders die Violine, die Mandoline, die Gitarre, das Saxophon und das Harmonium. Die

Tanpura (*Tambura* im Süden), ein Borduninstrument, hält den Grundton des Raga das ganze Konzert hindurch. Dieses Instrument wurde schon seit langer Zeit benutzt, obwohl der erste bildhauerische Nachweis erst aus dem 9. Jahrhundert n. Chr. stammt, und ist ein Kennzeichen der indischen Musik. Die Verankerung im Grundton erlaubt unterschiedliche tonale Muster, komplexe Verzierungen und rhythmische Berech-nungen, schließt aber Modulationen, an die das westliche Ohr gewöhnt ist, aus. Daher wirkt der Klang, der von westlichen Musikern, die diese Stücke spielen, erzeugt wird, anfänglich farblos, aber wenn die Gamakas, wie im Vorwort bereits erwähnt, angewendet werden, ist der veränderte Klang der Beginn eines veränderten Hörens.

Lernstrukturen

Südindien

Die Lernstruktur ist für die südindische Musik seit über 400 Jahren festgelegt. Purandaradasa, der als der Urvater der karnatischen Musik angesehen wird, ging dabei auf die Veränderungen ein, die die indische Musik durch den Einfluss der persischen Kultur der Mughals erfuhr. Er legte die ersten Übungen und Lieder fest, die die Studenten lernen sollten, um die Merkmale des karnatischen Raga und Tala zu verstehen. Beispiele aus diesem „Lehrplan" bilden die Grundlage für die karnatischen Musikstücke in diesem Buch. Zuerst kommen Beispiele für tonleiterartige Übungen (*Sarali Varisai* und *Janta Varisai*) und rhythmische Übungen (*Alankara*). Diese werden in drei unterschiedlichen Tempi ausgeführt, wobei Handzeichen helfen, den Tala zu halten. Auf diese Weise wird ein durchgängiger Puls geschaffen, der das Viertel-, Achtel- und Sechzehnteltempo kontrolliert. (Das Tempo wächst mit steigender Fertigkeit.)

Als nächstes werden einfache Lieder (*Gitams*) eingeführt, schlichte Melodien, die von Anfang bis Ende in einem Tempo gesungen werden. Danach folgen rhythmische Kompositionen (*Svarajatis*), die aus *Pallavi* und *Charana* zusammengestellt wurden, wie in Chor- und Versschemata. Daran anschließend werden Ragastudien (*Varnams*) gelernt, die das Herausbilden der Melodielinie zeigen, wie es für den Raga kennzeichnend ist. Diese werden in zwei, manchmal drei Tempi gespielt. Das wiederum führt schließlich zu Kompositionen (*Kirtanas*). In einem *Kirtana* gibt es drei musikalische Themen, wobei das erste quasi nach Art eines Refrains wiederholt wird. Da ein Konzert mit einem Tanzstück (*Tillana*) endet, wurde dieses auch noch in dieses Buch mit aufgenommen.

Durch diese Methode, sich das Material selbst zu erarbeiten, wird Vertrautheit mit verschiedenen Ragas gewonnen. Davon ausgehend beginnt der Student dann seine oder ihre eigene Musik zu machen, und zwar mit Hilfe von Improvisationen, die das Tonmaterial des Raga benutzen. Diese erscheinen als freie Improvisation (*Alapana*) vor der Komposition, als rhythmische Improvisation (*Kalpana Svara*) nach der gelernten Komposition oder an ausgewählten Stellen innerhalb der Komposition.

Nordindien

In der nordindischen Musik ist die Lernmethode vielfältiger, je nach *Gharana*, dem jeweiligen Singstil (dieser wird normalerweise nach der Provinz oder der Stadt, in der gesungen wird, benannt) oder dem Guru, der den Student in seinem Haus zum Erlernen der Disziplin aufnimmt. Diese Gurukula – Sishyalernmethode war auch im Süden vorherrschend, aber dort gab es mehr Übereinstimmung über das, was gelehrt werden sollte. Im Norden unternahm zu Beginn des letzten Jahrhunderts der Musikwissenschaftler Pandit Bhatkhande den Versuch, die Namen und den Inhalt der Ragas zu vereinheitlichen. Er schrieb auch viele didaktische Lieder in verschiedenen Ragas, um die Stimmung jener Ragas (*Lakshana Geet*) einzufangen – ganz ähnlich wie Purandaradasa.

Der hindustanische Raga ist in unterschiedlichen Improvisationsstilen kunstvoll ausgearbeitet, wobei vorgegebene Muster und Strukturen verwendet werden. Für die Sitar und das instrumentale Spiel werden diese *Alap*, *Jor* und *Jhal* genannt. In der Vokalmusik heißen die Improvisationsstile *Alap* und *Tans*, die unterschiedlichen Kompositionsstile *Dhrupad*, *Khyal* und *Thumri*.

Hörtradition

Hörtradition bedeutet in der indischen Musik, dass dasselbe Stück nur ganz selten zweimal auf genau dieselbe Art und Weise gespielt wird. Dieses Buch beinhaltet daher einen Querschnitt durch die Stücke, die ich entweder in der karnatischen Tradition gelernt habe, oder die von den hindustanischen Lehrern am Bhavan für die hindustanische Tradition ausgewählt wurden. Diese Manuskriptvorlage ist, wie alle Notationen, die für indische Musik benutzt werden, eine gerüstartige Erinnerungshilfe, die den Rahmen für eine individuelle Interpretation von Gamaka und melodischen Variationen darstellt. Von mir ausgeschriebene Gamakas sind nur ein Anfangsversuch, der Melodielinie indische Würze zu verleihen.

Eine Trommel ist normalerweise sowohl beim nord- als auch beim südindischen Musikvortrag Teil des Ensembles, da der Tala eine wichtige musikalische Komponente darstellt. Der Bordun ist ebenfalls typisch für die indische Musik.

Die indische Violine

Die indische und die westliche Violine unterscheiden sich nur in der Stimmung ihrer Saiten. Im Süden ist die Violine sehr beliebt und taucht in allen karnatischen Vokalkonzerten als Begleitinstrument auf. Sie hat auch ihren festen Platz als Soloinstrument, wobei sie ihre Beliebtheit dem tragenden Ton, der durch den Bogen erzeugt wird, und ihrer Ähnlichkeit zur Stimme durch die Fingerbewegung der linken Hand verdankt. In der hindustanischen Musik, aus der ursprünglich unter dem Einfluss der persischen Musiker und Förderer eine größere Vielfalt an Saiteninstrumenten hervorging (wie z.B. die Sitar, die Sarod und die Sarangi), ist sie erst in der letzten Zeit beliebter geworden.

Um 1790 wurde die Violine erstmals durch Mitglieder der Musikkapelle der East India Company in Madras in die indische Musikwelt eingeführt, wobei deren Geiger oftmals Iren waren. Die Tatsache, dass eine der frühesten karnatischen Violinen aus der Mitte des 19. Jahrhunderts als Fiddle Ponnusami bekannt wurde, unterstützt die wahrscheinliche Herkunft dieses Instruments. Balusvami Dikshitar (1786 – 1859), der jüngere Bruder des bedeutenden Komponisten Muttusvami Dikshitar (1775 – 1835), erlernte das Violinspiel in Madras und wurde dann Hofmusiker in Ettaiyapuram. Über die Jahre wurde die Spieltechnik modifiziert, um der eher meditativen Tonqualität und der flüssigen Handhabung der linken Hand zu entsprechen.

Haltung

Um die Violine in der richtigen Stellung zu halten, sitzt man mit gekreuzten Beinen, wobei die Schnecke der Violine auf dem Knöchel des rechten Fußes ruht. Das erleichtert das Aufsetzen der Finger der linken Hand und man hat nicht das Problem, die Violine unter dem Kinn halten zu müssen wie bei der westlichen Technik.

Die Tongebung

Obwohl sie klar sein soll, erfordert die Tonqualität bei indischer Musik nicht denselben Grad an Tonvolumen wie die westliche Musik. Am Anfang werden hauptsächlich die oberen zwei Saiten (gleichzusetzen mit A und E) zum Spielen der Melodien benutzt. Deshalb kann die Bogenhaltung mehr wie in der Volksmusik sein, ohne dass man dem gekrümmten Daumen oder dem gebogenen kleinen Finger, die so wesentlich zur westlichen Art der Artikulation und ihrem Tonvolumen beitragen, größere Aufmerksamkeit zu schenken braucht. Zur Zeit verwenden indische Violinisten Mikrofone oder, in zunehmenden Maße, elektrische Violinen für ihre Aufführungen. Obwohl man sich darüber streiten kann, ob das den eigentlichen Ton verzerrt, erlaubt es einen entspannteren Umgang mit der rechten Handhaltung. Der Spieler braucht zudem kein Vibrato.

Die Stimmung

Die Saiten sind viel lockerer gespannt als auf einer westlichen Violine, weil die Tonhöhe, die zur Begleitung der Sänger erforderlich ist, niedriger ist – im Allgemeinen mindestens um eine Terz. Das erlaubt den Fingern, sanfter über die Saiten zu gleiten. Die Saiten sind auf tiefes Doh und Soh, dann Doh und Soh gestimmt. Das entspricht dem f und c1 sowie dem f1 und c2. Die gespannteren Saiten der westlichen Stimmung erlauben der Geige, voller zu klingen und durch die Bogentechnik eine größere Bandbreite an Dynamik und Artikulation. Der feste Zugriff der linken Hand in der westlichen Technik erzeugt ein größeres Volumen und Vibrato. All das gehört nicht zum indischen Klang. Nordindische Geiger benutzen allerdings manchmal eine westliche Stimmung und legen sie dann als tiefes Ma, Sa, Pa und hohes Ri fest. Das ermöglicht ihnen eine größere Bandbreite an Noten und einen runderen Ton.

Verzierungen

Die indischen Verzierungen erfordern ein sehr ausgeprägtes „Gefühl" in der linken Hand, um eine volle Entfaltung der Verzierungskunst im indischen Stil zu erhalten. Es muß mit Lockerheit und Wendigkeit gepaart sein, um kleinere und größere Entfernungen von und hin zur Hauptnote zu gleiten (einige Geiger reiben ihre Finger sogar mit Öl ein, um das zu erleichtern). Der Drang nach Verzierung ist ein wesentlicher Teil der indischen Seele. Aus diesem Grund wurde ein System für Verzierungszeichen entwickelt, das erstmals Subbarama Dikshitar (der Enkel des bereits erwähnten Violinisten Balusvami Dikshitar) in seinem 1904 veröffentlichten Telugu-Traktat *Sangita Sampradaya Pradarsini* einführte. Diese Notation wurde von Smt. Vidya Shankar in ihrem Buch *The Art and Science of Carnatic Music* weiterentwickelt (veröffentlicht 1986 von der Madras Music Academy) und bildet die Grundlage für die Zeichen, die in diesem Buch verwendet werden.

Westliche Musiker, die sich zum ersten Mal mit dieser Musik auseinandersetzen, können das mit einer westlich gestimmten Violine tun, aber es wird dadurch schwieriger. Für den westlichen Violinisten, der es gelernt hat, seine Finger zwecks sicherer Intonation fest an ihrem Platz zu halten, mag sich das Handrutschen unnatürlich anfühlen, aber der Triller- oder Verzierungseffekt ist dazu da, den Raga zu verschönern. Trotzdem ist die Intonation sehr wichtig und spiegelt die Stimmung und die Eigenheit des Raga wider. Sie wird unterstützt durch den Bordun, der die ganze Aufführung lang durchklingt.

An einigen Stellen habe ich Fingersätze vorgeschlagen, um dem Anfänger zu helfen, sich dem indischen Konzept der miteinander verbundenen Noten zu nähern. Es ist darauf angelegt, das Ohr vom Auge zu trennen, damit der Ton nicht so gestelzt klingt, wie die westliche Notation das mit dem Setzen der einzelnen Finger vorgibt. Auf der anderen Seite wird das Gleiten den Druck von den Fingern der linken Hand wegnehmen.

Wenn möglich wäre es sehr hilfreich, die Geige um einen Ton herunterzustimmen. Die tiefergestimmten Saiten machen einen wesentlichen Unterschied in der Tonqualität aus, da sie einen weicheren Ton erzeugen. Für eine südindische Stimmung würde man das nur mit der A- und der E- Saite tun, was folgende Stimmung ergäbe: g, d1, g1, d2. In diesem Falle haben die Finger allerdings nicht mehr dieselbe Funktion, weshalb es leichter fällt, die *Sargam* Notation zu benutzen.

Texterklärungen

○ **Notennamen**

Die Sargam Notation benutzt den Anfangsbuchstaben oder die Anfangssilbe der 7 indischen Notennamen:

S	Sa	(wie in „ja")	Shadja
R	Ri	(wie in „nie")	Rishabha
G	Ga	(wie in „ja")	Gandhara
M	Ma	(wie in „ja")	Madhyama
P	Pa	(wie in „ja")	Panchama
D	Dha	(wie in „ja")	Dhaivata
N	Ni	(wie in „nie")	Nishadha

In der anschließenden Sargam-Notation habe ich die Notenlängen folgendermaßen angezeigt:

Sa	= Viertelnote
sa	= Achtelnote
s	= Sechzehntelnote

Pausen werden als Satzzeichen dargestellt:

;	= Viertelpause
,	= Achtelpause
.	= Sechzehntelpause

Ein Punkt über einer Note bezieht sich auf die nächsthöhere Oktave, ein Punkt darunter entsprechend auf die nächsttiefere.

○ **Südindische Sargam Terminologie**

Wo Zahlen hinter den Notennamen erscheinen, beziehen sie sich auf die erniedrigte bzw. erhöhte Note. Das entspricht der enharmonischen Stimmung, die ein westlicher Violinist z.B. zwischen e und fes erkennen würde. Die Stellung der Note in Bezug auf Sa ist besonders wichtig, wenn sie mit einem Bordun erklingt.

Wenn Sa = D, dann ist
Ri_1 = Es	Ga_1 = Fes	Ma_1 = G
Ri_2 = E	Ga_2 = F	Ma_2 = Gis
Ri_3 = Eis	Ga_3 = Fis	

○ **Der karnatische Rhythmus**

Das richtige Zählsystem besteht aus einzelnen Blöcken mit Zählstrukturen. Die einleitenden drei sind:

1. der *Anudrutam* = ein Schlag;
2. der *Drutam* = ein Schlag plus einer wellenförmigen Handbewegung [im Folgenden als Welle bezeichnet, Anm. d. Ü.];
3. der *Laghu* = ein Schlag plus Zählen mit den Fingern, wobei man mit dem kleinen Finger beginnt. Die Menge des Zählens ist dabei variabel. In diesem Buch kommen Talas vor, bei denen mit 2 und mit 3 Fingern gezählt wird.

Adi Tala: 4 + 2 + 2 =
1	2	3	4	5	6	7	8

Schlag, kleiner Finger, Ringfinger, Mittelfinger, Schlag, Welle, Schlag, Welle. (s. Seiten 58 und 59)

Rupaka Tala: 2 + 4 =
1	2	3	4	5	6

Schlag, Welle, Schlag, kleiner Finger, Ringfinger, Mittelfinger

Misra Chapu: 3 + 2 + 2 =
1	2	3	4	5	6	7

Schlag, kleiner Finger, Ringfinger, Schlag, Welle, Schlag, Welle

○ **Der hindustanische Rhythmus**

In diesem Buch werden 3 Talas benutzt.
Tin Tal = 16 Schläge
Das Zählsystem für den Tin Tal oder die 16 Schläge kann mit den inneren Falten der 4 Fingerglieder angezeigt werden, wobei man mit dem kleinen Finger beginnt. Das übliche Muster ist es allerdings, den Schlag auf jedem 4. Schlag anzuzeigen, und zwar mit einmal Klatschen (=kl) auf dem 1., 5. und 13. Schlag sowie einer Welle auf dem 9. Schlag:

x				x				0				x			
1	2	3	4	5	6	7	8	9	10	11	12	13	14	15	16
Kl	2	3	4	Kl	2	3	4	Welle	2	3	4	Kl	2	3	4

Rupak Tal = 7 Schläge
Die 7 Schläge hier werden genauso wie die karnatische Misra Chapu geschlagen.

Deepchandi Tal = 14 Schläge

0		x		x		0			x		x		
1	2	3	4	5	6	7	8	9	10	11	12	13	14

Passagen zum Improvisieren schließen normalerweise eine Tihai mit ein und enden auch mit einer. Die Tihai ist ein dreimal wiederholtes Schema.

Wenn Pa = A, dann ist
Dha_1 = B	Ni_1 = Ces
Dha_2 = H	Ni_2 = C
Dha_3 = His	Ni_3 = Cis

○ **Nordindische Sargam Teminologie**

Wo Noten unterstrichen sind, werden sie von ihrer normalen oder erhöhten Tonleiterposition aus erniedrigt, wenn darüber ein Akzent erscheint (nur bei Ma), wird die Note erhöht. Es muss auch beachtet werden, dass Ri als Re (wie in 'Reh') gesungen wird.

Wenn Sa = D, dann ist
<u>Re</u> = Es	<u>Ga</u> = F	Ma = G
Re = E	Ga = Fis	Má = Gis

Wenn Pa = A, dann ist
<u>Dha</u> = B	<u>Ni</u> = C
Dha = H	Ni = Cis

Sowohl die nord- als auch die südindische Musik benutzt den Sargam, um die tonale Welt des Raga und die rhythmische Genauigkeit der einzelnen Phrasen zu entfalten. Beim Singen werden auch Silben wie z.B. *ta da na* verwendet.

Zu Beginn jeder Ragakomposition wird der *Arohana* (aufsteigendes Muster) und *Avarohana* (absteigendes Muster) mit Bezug auf diese *Sargam* Terminologie angegeben. Diese Noten werden benutzt, um den Raga durch eine Improvisation vor Beginn der Komposition zu vervollkommnen. Unter den Noten steht auch ein Text, da die indische Musik von der vokalen Tradition abstammt. Die Instrumente ahmen die Stimme so gut wie möglich nach.

○ **Der Rhythmus**

Die Taktart für jede Komposition wird beim Singen mit Handzeichen angezeigt oder vom Publikum, während die Künstler spielen! Das bedeutet, dass unregelmäßige Taktschläge durch Handzeichen angezeigt werden. Ich habe westliche Taktzeichen verwendet, um das Lesen zu erleichtern.

Glossar

Ein Glossar am Ende des Buches erklärt die hier verwendeten indischen Begriffe.

Karnatische Musik

In der Karnatischen Musik spielen Kompositionen eine wichtige Rolle. Es gibt unterschiedliche Formen, von denen einige in diesem Buch enthalten sind. Jede Komposition fängt die Stimmung und das Gefühl des jeweiligen Raga ein. Ich möchte mich für die Hilfe bedanken, die ich sowohl von den Bhavan Lehrern als auch von Professor T. V. Gopalakrishnan für diesen Abriss über karnatische Musik bekommen habe.

Ragas in karnatischer Musik

Der Raga ist eine Abfolge von Noten, die die Melodielinie festlegen. Es gibt Hunderte von unterschiedlichen Ragas sowohl in der nord- als auch in der südindischen Musik. Einige von ihnen sind sehr alt, andere wurden erst in jüngster Zeit erdacht. Alle Ragas werden zu Raga-Familien zusammengestellt.

In Südindien gibt es ein Klassifizierungssystem für Ragas, das seine abschließende Form im 18. Jahrhundert durch Govindacharya erhielt. Innerhalb jedes Tetrachords einer Oktave mit einer reinen Quinte (Doh Soh) deckt dieses alle vorstellbaren Kombinationen ab, sowohl von Ganztönen und Halbtönen als auch übermäßigen Tonschritten, wobei auf- wie abwärts dieselben 7 Noten verwendet werden. Diese Kombinationen nennt man die 72 *Melakarta* (wörtl. „Gruppenbildner").

Untergeordnet unter diese sogenannten *Janaka* oder „Elterntonleitern" werden alle *Janya* oder „Tochter-Ragas" gesammelt: das sind Ragas, die Variationen der linearen Notenabfolge von den „Eltern Mela" darstellen. Es gibt 3 Haupttypen von *Janya* Ragas:

Asampurna = „unvollständig"(d.h. nicht alle sieben Noten) Ragas, die weniger oder mehr als sieben Noten in der Aufwärts- oder Abwärtsbewegung haben, wie z.B. bei den ersten zwei Liedern im Malahari Raga (S. 26, 28).
Vakra = Ragas, die einen „Zick-Zack"-Weg in der Aufwärts- oder Abwärtsbewegung benutzen, wie z.B. der Suposhini Raga (S. 41).
Bhashanga = Ragas mit einer „fremden" Note, die selten aber gezielt eingeschoben wird.

Oft ist der *Janya* Raga älter als der klassifizierte Raga, so dass es keinen Grund gibt, den *Janya* gegenüber dem *Janaka* abzuwerten. 'Eltern' ist also ein sehr irreführender Begriff. Einige Ragas bestehen aus mehr als sieben Noten. Der Bhairavi in der hindustanischen Musik benutzt z.B. alle 12 Noten, allerdings nicht nacheinander wie in einer chromatischen Tonleiter. Ebenso verwenden verschiedene Ragas auch verschiedene Schattierungen ein und derselben Note. Der **Varali** (D Es Fes Gis A B Cis D) aus der karnatischen Musik benutzt z.B. eine höhere 4. Note, Ma oder Gis, als der **Kalyani** (D E Fis Gis A H Cis D).

Der Bezug zu Tages- und Jahreszeit, der für einige Ragas in der karnatischen Musik wichtig ist, ist in der hindustanischen Tradition sehr viel bedeutender. „Bhava" oder die „Stimmung" spielt eine Schlüsselrolle in den Raga-Aufführungen der karnatischen Musik und spiegelt die Bedeutung der Texte wider, die sich mit der Suche der Seele nach Gott befassen. Bhava ist auch in der hindustanischen Musik sehr wichtig.

Kompositionen

Es gibt Ragas mit Hunderten von Kompositionen und andere mit nur einer. Obwohl die Kompositionen von Purandaradas aus dem 15. Jahrhundert Teil der karnatischen Tradition sind, war es erst die Dreiheit der karnatischen Komponisten Tyagaraja, Dikshitar und Syama Sastri im 18. und 19. Jahrhundert, die das Kernrepertoire von dem begründeten, was wir heute unter karnatischer Musik verstehen. Viele Kompositionen sind seitdem zu diesem Repertoire hinzugefügt worden. Ihre Texte sind meist in der klassischen Sprache Indiens, dem Sanskrit geschrieben, aber auch in Telugu und Tamil, zwei mundartlichen Sprachen des Südens. Drei von Tyagarajas Kompositionen sind in dieses Buch aufgenommen worden. Die Improvisationen, die vor, nach und an bestimmten Stellen innerhalb der Stücke stattfinden, würden den Rahmen dieses Buches sprengen.

Verzierungen oder Gamakas

In der karnatischen Musik sind die Gamakas eher als ein fester Bestandteil der Tonleiter denn als ein zusätzliches Merkmal zu be-zeichnen. Was zwischen den Noten passiert ist genauso wichtig wie die Noten selbst.

Da es sich hier um ein einführendes Werk in die indische Musik handelt, habe ich Zeichen nach Art der barocken Verzierungen verwendet. In den ersten zwei Kirtana habe ich die Gamakas jedoch in Annäherung an die westliche Notation, ausgeschrieben, damit die Kirtana nicht wie die westliche Darbietung einer modalen Weise erklingt, sondern sich zum „indischen Klang" hinbewegt. Es gibt mehrere Versionen der Gamakas und Hinführungen zur indischen Verzierungstechnik – wie z.B. jene, die von Prof. Sambamoorthy vorgelegt wurden, aber sehr wenige Lehrer beziehen sich namentlich auf sie und verschiedene Musiker haben von ihnen ihre eigene, individuelle Interpretation.

Um aus dem Lehrwerk *Natya Sastra* der Kapazität Bharata, der im 3. Jahrhundert n. Chr. lebte, zu zitieren:

Ein Raga ohne raffiniert verzierte Merkmale ist wie eine mondlose Nacht, eine Kletterpflanze ohne Blumen, ein Fluss ohne Wasser, eine Frau ohne Juwelen.

Daher ist das Bemühen um Verzierung sowohl ein Teil der indischen Musik als auch eines ihrer Geschenke, wenn man sich mit ihr beschäftigt. In der Notation indischer Musik gibt es allerdings nur selten Hinweise auf die Gamakas; normalerweise werden sie über das Gehör vom Lehrer gelernt. In der Sargam-Notation wird eine indische Komposition mit dem Zusatz von Kommas zum Verlängern von Noten sowie unterstrichenen Noten zu ihrer Beschleunigung versehen (s. S. 18). Es gibt einen Tala (Takteinheit), in den die Hauptnoten hineinpassen und der als gerüstartige Erinnerungshilfe bei der Melodie dient.

In diesem Versuch, indische Musik für westliche Musiker in schriftlicher Form zugänglich zu machen, sind Kompromisse bei der genauen Darstellung von Verzierungen unvermeidlich. Durch das Hören von Live-Konzerten mit großen indischen Musikern wird es dem Leser leichter fallen, eine zufriedenstellende Antwort zu finden. Noch besser wäre es, tatsächlich einen indischen Musiklehrer zu finden.

Traditionell wird den Studenten zuerst der **Mayamalavagaula** Raga beigebracht. Dieser hat ein passendes Muster für Übungen, die die Haltung des ersten Fingers betreffen: die Noten folgen paarweise in Halbtonschritten aufeinander - SaRi GaMa PaDha NiSa - und sind auf jeder Saite durch einen übermäßigen Tonschritt voneinander getrennt. Er ist der Elternraga für den **Malahari**, zu dem die ersten Lieder gehören (ein *Asampurna Janya* Raga, der aus fünf Noten aufwärts und sechs Noten abwärts besteht – D Es G A B D D B A G Fis Es D). Diese Ragaauswahl wurde vermutlich getroffen, weil Purandaradasa ein Vinaspieler war und diese Intervalle leichter zu spielen als zu singen sind.

Sarasvati, the Goddess of Music, Art and Learning
Sarasvati, déesse de la Musique, des Arts et de l'Instruction
Sarasvati, die Göttin der Musik, Kunst und des Lernens

Preliminary guide to Ornaments or *Gamakas*

Guide préliminaire des ornements ou *gamakas*

Eine erste Richtschnur für die Verzierungen oder *Gamakas*

2

Listen to the first track of the CD. The ornaments are played first by a western violinist, followed by an Indian violinist.

Ecoutez la première plage du CD. Les ornements y sont exécutés d'abord par un violoniste occidental puis par un violoniste indien.

Hören Sie die Nummer 1 auf der CD an. Die Verzierungen werden zuerst von einem westlichen Violinisten und dann von einem indischen gespielt.

Kampita
shake
a gentle wave between two notes (generally the note and its lower neighbour which is called the *anusvara*)

kampita
tremblement
légère oscillation entre deux notes (généralement la note et sa voisine la plus grave appelée *anusvara*)

Kampita
Triller
eine sanfte Welle zwischen zwei Noten (üblicherweise die Note und ihr darunterliegender Nachbar – *Anusvara* genannt)

Nokku
descending pull
pulling down from the note above

nokku
pincement descendant
pincement inférieur effectué à partir de la note supérieure

Nokku
absteigendes Ziehen
von der oberen Note nach unten ziehen

Pratyahata
strike back
like a mordent

pratyahata
retour en arrière
comme un mordant

Pratyahata
Rückschlag
wie ein Mordent

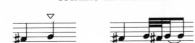

Sphurita
throbbing
pair of notes, with stress on the 2nd

sphurita
lancé
répétition avec accent sur la deuxième note

Sphurita
hämmernd
zwei Noten mit Betonung auf der zweiten Note

Etrajaru
upward slide

etrajaru
glissement vers le haut

Etrajaru
aufwärtsgerichtetes Gleiten

Irakkajaru
downwards slide

irakkajaru
glissement vers le bas

Irakkajaru
abwärtsgerichtetes Gleiten

Orikkai
snap
stopping a note with a brief
touch of a higher note

orikkai
claquement
interruption d'une note par l'attaque
brève d'une note plus aiguë

Orikkai
Schnappen
das Beenden einer Note mit der kurzen
Berührung einer höheren Note

Ravai
brief repetition
by touching another note in between
intermediate note written above

ravai
répétition brève
avec ajout d'une note brève plus aiguë
entre les notes répétées

Ravai
kurze Wiederholung
das Berühren einer dazwischen liegen-
den Note, die über der Hauptnote
notiert wird

Odukkal
note pushed aside
often occurs in joining two adjacent
notes

odukkal
note poussée de côté
souvent pour joindre deux notes
adjacentes

Odukkal
zur Seite gedrückte Note
tritt oft beim Verbinden zweier benach-
barter Noten auf

Sarali Varisai

first lesson exercises/exercices de la première leçon/Erste Lektion, Übungen

Like scales and arpeggios for western musicians these exercises are the staple practice material for all Karnatic musicians. They are played at three speeds, beginning in Mayamalavagaula Raga in Adi Tala (8 beats).

A l'image des gammes et des arpèges des musiciens occidentaux, ces exercices représentent l'entraînement fondamental de tous les musiciens carnatiques. On les joue selon trois vitesses différentes en commençant par le raga *mayamalavagaula* dans le tala *adi* (8 pulsations).

Wie die Tonleitern und Arpeggien für die westlichen Musiker, so sind diese Übungen das hauptsächliche Übungsmaterial für alle karnatischen Musiker. Sie werden in drei verschiedenen Geschwindigkeiten gespielt, wobei man mit dem Mayamalavagaula Raga im Adi Tala (8 Schläge) beginnt.

Basic tips for making an Indian sound

- No vibrato
- Light bow strokes, tending towards the upper half of the bow
- Sit cross legged on the floor without shoes
- Lighten left hand fingers
- Tuning instrument down slackens the string pressure

Conseils de base pour obtenir une sonorité indienne

- pas de vibrato
- coups d'archets légers, plutôt dans la partie supérieure de l'archet
- position assise le sol (sans chaussures)
- pression légère des doigts de la main gauche
- accord plus grave de l'instrument pour relâcher la tension des cordes

Grundsätzliche Ratschläge, um einem indischen Ton zu erzeugen

- kein Vibrato
- leichte Bogenstriche, eher in der oberen Hälfte des Bogens
- auf dem Fußboden sitzend spielen (ohne Schuhe)
- die Finger der linken Hand lockern
- das Instrument herunterstimmen, um den Saitendruck zu vermindern

ornaments used:

⋀	*kampita*	= shake
w	*nokku*	= descending pull
\	*irakkajaru*	= downwards slide
▽	*pratyahata*	= strike back

ornements utilisés:

⋀	*kampita*	= tremblement
w	*nokku*	= pincement descendant
\	*irakkajaru*	= glissement vers le bas
▽	*pratyahata*	= retour en arrière

benutzte Verzierungen:

⋀	*kampita*	= Triller
w	*nokku*	= absteigendes Ziehen
\	*irakkajaru*	= abwärtsgerichtetes Gleiten
▽	*pratyahata*	= Rückschlag

3

Mayamalavagaula Raga

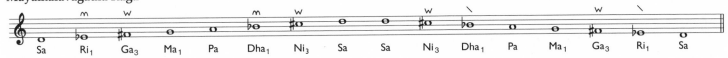

3 With ornaments notated

Rhythmic exercises/exercices rythmiques/Rhythmische Übungen

Janta Varisai

second lesson exercises/exercices de la deuxième leçon/Zweite Lektion, Übungen

Purandaradasa
(1485–1560)

Mayamalavagaula Raga in Adi Tala

Rhythmic exercises/exercices rythmiques/Rhythmische Übungen

Alankara: Dhruva

Counting pattern: 4+2+4+4 / formule mesurée: 4+2+4+4 / Zählschema: 4+2+4+4

Mayamalavagaula Raga

Sri Gananatha

in praise of Ganesh/à la louange de Ganesh/Lobgesang auf Ganesh

Purandaradasa
(1485–1560)

Malahari Raga in Tala Rupaka

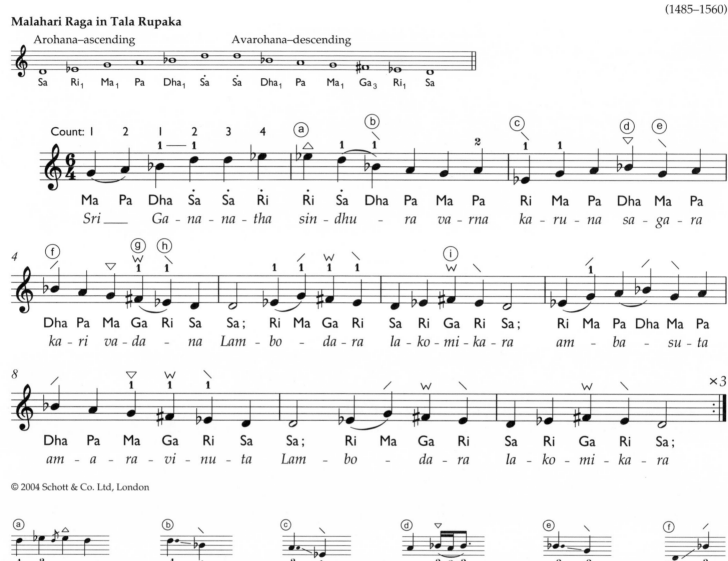

Indian Sargam Notation/notation indienne *sargam*/Indische Sargam Notation

Sri Gananatha

Malahari Raga/raga *malahari*/Malahari Raga

(as written in western notation opposite)
(transcription occidentale en regard)
(wie auf S. 26 in westlicher Notation geschrieben)

Raga notes: Sa Ri₁ Ma₁ Pa Dha₁ Ṡa   Ṡa Dha₁ Pa Ma₁ Ga₃ Ri₁ Sa

Sargam:	Ma Pa Dha Ṡa Ṡa Ri | Ri Sa Dha Pa Ma Pa | Ri Ma Pa Dha Ma Pa |
Lyrics:	Sri ___ Ga - na - na - tha sin - dhu – ra var - na ka - ru - na sa - ga - ra

Dha Pa Ma Ga Ri Sa | Sa ; Ri Ma Ga Ri | Sa Ri Ga Ri Sa ; | Ri Ma Pa Dha Ma Pa |
ka - ri va - da – na Lam - bo - da - ra la - ko - mi - ka - ra am - ba - su - ta

Dha Pa Ma Ga Ri Sa | Sa ; Ri Ma Ga Ri | Sa Ri Ga Ri Sa ; ‖
am - a - ra - vi - nu - ta Lam - bo - da - ra la - ko - mi - ka - ra

In the *Ganamrutha Bodhini* book for Karnatic students printed in Madras (1989) this song is laid out thus:

Dans le recueil *Ganamrutha Bodhini* destiné aux étudiants carnatiques publié à Madras (1989), ce chant apparaît ainsi:

In dem Buch *Ganamrutha Bodhini* für karnatische Studenten (1989 in Madras gedruckt) ist dieses Lied folgendermaßen gestaltet:

Sargam:	M	P	| D	Ṡ	Ṡ	Ṙ	‖ Ṙ	Ṡ	| D	P	M	P	‖
Lyrics:	Sri ___		Ga	- na	- na	- tha	sin	- dhu	–	- ra	var	- na	

	R	M	| P	D	M	P	‖ D	P	| M	G	R	S	‖
	Ka	- ru	- na	sa	- ga	- ra	ka	- ri	va	- dha	–	- na	

	S	,	| R	M	G	R	‖ S	R	| G	R	S	,	‖
	Lam	–	- bo	–	- da	- ra	la	- ko	- mi	- ka	- ra		

	R	M	| P	D	M	P	‖ D	P	| M	G	R	S	‖
	Am	–	- ba	–	- su	- ta	a	- ma	- ra	- vi	- nu	- ta	

	S	,	| R	M	G	R	‖ S	R	| G	R	S	,	‖
	Lam	–	- bo	–	- da	- ra	la	- ko	- mi	- ka	- ra		

Meaning: O Lord Ganesh, who likes the colour red and is the ocean of mercy, praise to you.

Traduction: O Seigneur Ganesh, toi qui aimes la couleur rouge et es un océan de miséricorde, louange à toi!

Bedeutung: Oh Gott Ganesh, der die Farbe rot liebt und ein Meer an Barmherzigkeit ist, dir sei Lob gesungen.

8

Padumanabha

Name of Vishnu/Nom de Vishnou/Name des Vishnu

Purandaradasa
(1485–1560)

Malahari Raga in Misra Chapu Tala

Arohana   Avarohana

Sa Ri₁ Ma₁ Pa Dha₁ Ṡa   Ṡa Dha₁ Pa Ma₁ Ga₃ Ri₁ Sa

Count: 1 2 3 1 2 1 2

Ri Sa Dha Sa; Sa;   Ma Ga Ri Ma Ma Pa;   Sa Dha; Dha Pa Ma Pa   Dha Dha Pa Ma Ga Ri Sa

Pa - du - ma - na - bha   pa - ra - ma - pu - ru - sha   Pa - ram - jyo - ti - sva - ru - pa _____
Vi - du - ra - van - dya   vi - ma - la cha - ri - ta   vi - hang - ga - dhi - ro - ha - na _____

5

Pa Ma Pa Dha Ṡa Dha Ṡa   Ri Ṡa Dha Dha Ṡa Dha Pa   Dha Dha Pa Pa;   Pa Ma

U - da - di ni va - sa   u - ra - ga sa - ya - na   u - nna - to - na - ta -

8

Ri Ma Ma Pa;   Pa;   Dha Dha Pa Pa;   Pa Ma Ri;   Ma Ma Ga Ri Sa

- ma - hi - ma _____   Ya - du - ku lo - tta - ma - ya - jna - ra - ksha - ka

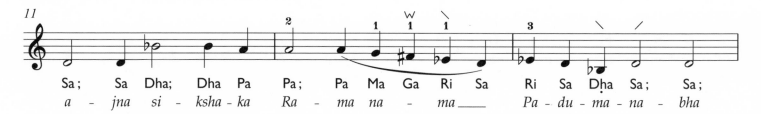

11

Sa;   Sa Dha; Dha Pa Pa;   Pa Ma Ga Ri Sa   Ri Sa Dha Sa;   Sa;

a - jna si - ksha - ka Ra - ma na - ma _____   Pa - du - ma - na - bha

14

Ma Ga Ri Ma Ma Pa;   Sa Dha; Dha Pa Ma Pa   Dha Dha Pa Ma Ga Ri Sa

pa - ra - ma - pu - ru - sha   Pa - ram - jyo - ti - sva - ru - pa _____

17

Ri Sa Dha Sa;   Sa;   Ri Sa Dha Sa;   Sa;   Ri Sa Dha Ri;;;   Sa;;;;;;

Pa - du - ma - na - bha   Pa - du - ma - na - bha   Pa - du - ma - na - bha _____

Vande Minakshi

M. Dikshitar
(c.1750–1830)
From/extrait de/aus: 'European airs and melodies'

9

Van - de Mi - na - kshi tvam sa - ra - si - ja vak - tre par - ne

Dur - ge na - ta su - ra bri - nde sa - kte gu - ru - gu - ha pa -

Fine

-li - ni ja - la ru - ha cha - ra - ne   Sun - da - ra pan - dya

nan - de ma - ye su - ri - ja - na - dha - re   sun - da - ra ra - ja sa -

D. C. al Fine

-ho - da - ri gow - ri   shu - bha - ka - ri sa - ta - tam a - ham

Muttusvami Dikshitar (brother of violinist Balusvami Dikshitar) adapted a number of western airs to the Karnatic tradition by writing Sanskrit words for the tunes. This one closely resembles the Irish folk-song 'The Rakes of Malloe'. Although the song uses the notes of the Sankarabharana Raga it does not have the authentic flavour of that raga.

Muttusvami Dikshitar (frère du violoniste Balusvami Dikshitar) adapta un certain nombre d'airs occidentaux à la tradition carnatique en écrivant des paroles en sanscrit sur ces mélodies. Celui-ci ressemble fortement à l'air traditionnel irlandais «The Rakes of Malloe». Bien qu'employant les notes du raga Sankarabharana, cet air n'en reflète pas la couleur authentique.

Muttusvami Dikshitar (Bruder des Violinisten Balusvami Dikshitar) passte eine Anzahl von westlichen Liedern an die karnatische Tradition an, indem er für die Melodien einen Text in Sanskrit schrieb. Die hier verwendete Melodie erinnert sehr stark an das irische Volkslied 'The Rakes of Malloe'. Obwohl das Lied die Noten des Sankarabharana Raga benutzt, gibt es nicht das authentische Gefühl dieses Ragas wieder.

Svarajati

Traditional

Bilahari Raga in Adi Tala

Study/étude/Studie

Varnam

11

Ramanath Srinivasa Iyengar

Mohana Raga in Adi Tala

* (repeat at double speed)

* rejouer en doublant la vitesse / in doppelter Geschwindigkeit wiederholen

Gaja Mukanai

In Praise of Ganesh/à la louange de Ganesh/Lobgesang auf Ganesh

T. V. Gopalkrishnan

Sankarabharana Raga in Adi Tala

*× = gliding fingers/glissement des doigts/gleitende Finger

This melody is based on words by D. Pattammal
Les paroles de cette mélodie sont de D. Pattammal
Dieser Melodie liegen Worte von D. Pattammal zugrunde

Kalaivani

In Praise of Sarasvati/à la louange de Sarasvati/Lobesang auf Sarasvati

T. V. Gopalakrishnan

Suddha dhanyasi Raga in Adi Tala

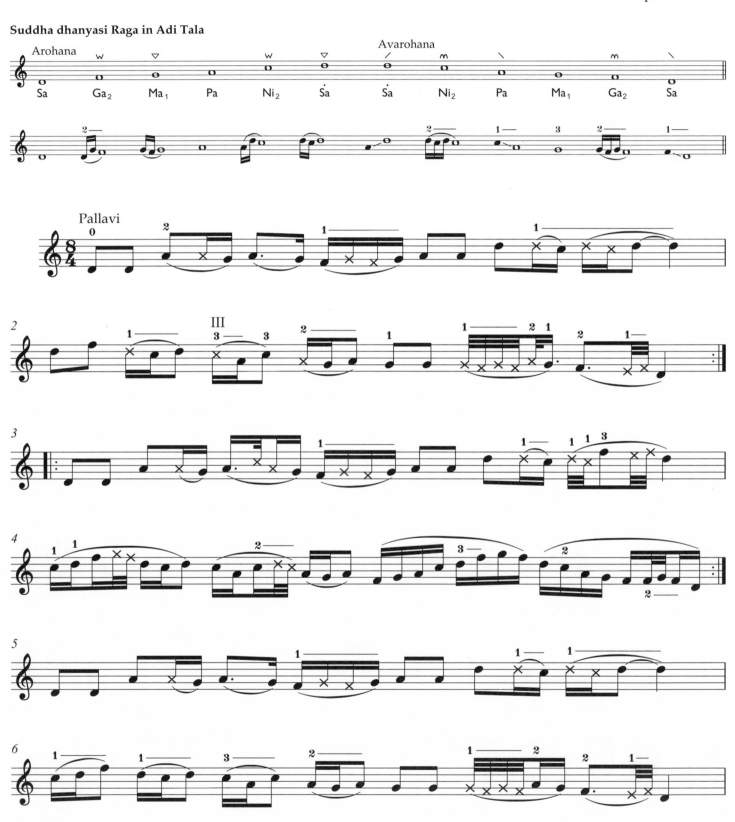

This melody is based on words by D. Pattammal
Les paroles de cette mélodie sont de D. Pattammal
Dieser Melodie liegen Worte von D. Pattammal zugrunde

Sarasvati is the Goddess of Art and Learning. She is usually depicted holding a vina.

Sarasvati est la déesse des arts et de l'instruction. Elle est généralement représentée tenant une vina.

Sarasvati ist die Göttin der Künste und des Lernens. Sie wird normalerweise mit einer Vina abgebildet.

Tatvameruga

That Thou Art*/Ce que tu es*/Dass Du Seist*

Sri Tyagaraja
(1767–1847)

Garudadhvani Raga in Adi Tala

Pallavi (with minimal gamakas)/Avec des gamakas minimaux/mit minimalen Gamakas

Ta - tvam-e - ru-ga   ta - ra   ma ___

Anupallavi

* The title expresses the non-dualist concept of the identity of the soul and God.

* Le titre exprime le concept non-dualiste de l'identité de l'âme et du Dieu.

* Der Titel drückt das non-dualistische Konzept der Identität von Seele und Gott aus.

15

Raminchuva

Come, O Beguiling One/Viens, o toi le séduisant/Oh komm, Verführer

Sri Tyagaraja
(1767–1847)

Suposhini Raga in Adi Tala tisra gati (8 × 3)

In this composition the zig-zag pattern of the raga is maintained throughout the phrases, hence the 'vakra' (crooked) nature of the melody. The tala, still 8 beats, has a triplet subdivision of each beat. This is called *tisra gati*: tisra = three; gati = gait, walk.

Dans cette composition, la formule en zig-zag du raga est constante dans toutes les phrases, d'où la nature *'vakra'* (brisée) de la mélodie. Les 8 pulsations du tala sont divisées en triolets, appelés *tisra gati*: tisra = trois, gati = marche.

In dieser Komposition wird das Zick-Zack-Muster des Ragas durch alle Phrasen hindurch beibehalten. Daher das 'vakra' (krumme) Wesen der Melodie. Der Tala, mit immer noch 8 Schlägen, hat bei jedem Schlag eine dreifache Unterteilung. Das wird *tisra gati* genannt: tisra = drei; gati = Gang, Schritt.

Sobhillu

16

The Beauty of the Seven Notes/La beauté des sept notes/Die Schönheit der sieben Noten

Sri Tyagaraja

Jaganmohini Raga in Rupaka Tala

Indian compositions are taught aurally and written down only as an aid to memory. This means that different teachers will pass on their own interpretations of the composition. This simplified version therefore sketches only the main outline of this melody. A fully notated version can be found in C. S. Ayyar's '120 Kritis of Sri Tyagaraja' (published 1959 in Sanskrit script). Our introduction and text use the same gamaka signs.

L'enseignement de la musique indienne est essentiellement oral et la notation des morceaux n'y sert que d'aide-mémoire. Chaque professeur transmettra, par conséquent, sa propre interprétation d'une composition. Cette version simplifiée n'indique que les contours principaux de cette mélodie. On en trouvera une transcription complète dans l'ouvrage de C. S. Ayyar: *120 Kritis of Sri Tyagaraja* (publié en 1959 selon la notation sanskrite). Notre introduction et notre notation de la pièce utilisent les mêmes signes de gamakas.

Indische Kompositionen werden mündlich tradiert. Eine Niederschrift ist höchstens als Gedächtnisstütze gedacht. Damit verbunden gibt jeder Lehrer seine eigene Interpretation der jeweiligen Komposition weiter. Deshalb skizziert diese vereinfachte Fassung nur die Grundzüge dieser Melodie. Eine vollständige Fassung findet sich in C. S. Ayyars "120 Kritis von Sri Tyagaraja" (1959 in Sanskrit veröffentlicht). Unsere Einleitung und Notation verwendet die selben Gamaka-Zeichen.

Tillana

Balamuralikrishna

Brindavani Raga in Tala Adi

North Indian
Hindustani Music

Hindustani raga and raga presentation is outlined here thanks to the generosity of the teachers of the Bharatiya Vidya Bhavan for the benefit of the reader.

Hindustani music relies heavily on improvisation. The compositions are short concise fragments of melody which capture the mood of the raga and serve to stimulate the imagination of the performing musician. To learn improvisation techniques in Indian music, guided examples are given by the teacher for the student to copy and from there to develop their own style, this school tradition is called Gharana. This perhaps shows why the teacher is such an important person in the Indian music student's development. The student's imagination becomes grounded in that of the teacher.

There are three main vocal forms:
1. **Dhrupad** is a slow classical form, it has a large improvised *alap* using syllables 'na' 'num' 'tum' derived from 'om'. This is followed by a short composition which has a very high literary value of devotional, mystical or philosophical content. This is then rendered in different speeds, double, triple and quadruple time, then the calculations are the creative venture of the musician and their interaction with the audience. Dhammar is a special type of Dhrupad which always has 14 beats divided 5+2+3+4 and is associated with Holi, Dhrupad can be in various tala cycles:12, 18, 22, 32 and so on.

2. **Khyal** is the most popular form and in it resides the largest number of short compositions in different ragas. It has has two sections: the *Sthayi* and *Antara*. These are usually two lines each and intersperse with improvised passages.

3. **Thumri** is a light classical form with much flamboyance of improvisation, usually sung towards the end of a concert.

The syllables employed in improvisation have their roots in the chanting of the Vedas. The later influence of Sufi musicians and the patronage of the Mughal court in turn was on instrumentation and treatment of ragas. On the accompanying CD, Pandit Vishwa Prakash and his students demonstrate an example of Dhrupad, Khyal and Thumri. (The *alap* and *tans* are improvisations prepared for his students.)

The sitar is the best known Indian instrument in the West and the style of instrumental raga presentation is shown here with *alap*, composition and *tans* composed and played by Sri Vijay Kumar Jagtap and his students.

Ragas are related to time both of the day and of the season, although the same raga can have different times for different musicians, some popular ragas are more widely recognised. For example:

Bhairav for early morning (D E♭ F♯ G A B♭ C♯ D)
Bhupali for late afternoon (D E F♯ A B D)
Malkauns for late night (D F G B♭ C D)
Miya Malhar for the rainy season (including D E F G A B C and C♯ D)

Ragas assigned to different times vary among gharanas or singing styles of musicians as do approaches to any one raga. However, the depth of feeling transmitted by the musician through the raga remains very strong according to their tradition.

The musicologist Bhatkhande at the beginning of the 20th century travelled around North India collecting and collating many ragas and raga compositions. He composed didactic raga songs called **Lakshana geet** to teach students the characteristics of the ragas. He also suggested ten *thaats* or popular scalar patterns under which to categorise ragas.

Musique hindoustanaise du nord de l'Inde

Le raga hindoustanais et sa présentation sont décrits ici grâce à la générosité des professeurs du centre Bharatiya Vidya Bhavan.

La musique hindoustanaise repose fortement sur l'improvisation. Les compositions y sont constituées de fragments mélodiques courts et concis expressifs du caractère du raga et servent à stimuler l'imagination de l'interprète. L'apprentissage des techniques d'improvisation de la musique indienne s'effectue sous la direction d'un maître dont le disciple imite les exemples avant de développer ensuite son propre style. Cette tradition d'enseignement, appelée gharana, explique l'importance du rôle du maître dans l'initiation du musicien indien. L'inspiration du disciple s'enracine dans celle du maître.

Il existe trois formes vocales principales :
1. Le **dhrupad** et le **dhammar** sont d'anciennes formes classiques dont l'*alap* improvisé utilise les syllabes 'na', 'num', 'tum' dérivées de la syllabe 'om'. Celui-ci est suivi d'une brève composition au contenu religieux, mystique ou philosophique de très haute valeur littéraire, interprétée à différents mouvements, double, triple et quadruple. Le choix des mesures rythmiques est ensuite laissé à l'interprète et à l'interaction du public. Le **dhammar**, associé à la fête Holi, comporte toujours 14 pulsations divisées selon le schéma 5 + 2+ 3 + 4 . Le **dhrupad** peut emprunter divers cycles de tala : 12, 18, 22, 32, etc.

2. Le **khyal** est la forme la plus répandue et comprend le plus grand nombre de compositions brèves sur différents ragas. Il est constitué de deux sections : le *sthayi* et l'*antara*, comportant généralement chacune deux lignes, qui s'intercalent entre les passages improvisés.

3. Le **thumri** est une forme classique légère, très brillante et improvisée, généralement chantée vers la fin du concert.

Les syllabes déployées dans l'improvisation trouvent leur origine dans la psalmodie des *vedas*. L'instrumentation et la manière de traiter les ragas subit l'influence plus récente des musiciens soufi et de la protection de la cour moghole. Sur le CD d'accompagnement, Pandit Vishwa Prakash et sa classe interprètent un exemple de *dhrupad*, de *khyal* et de *thumri* (l'*alap* et les *tans* sont ici des improvisations notées à l'intention de ses étudiants).

Le sitar est l'instrument indien le plus connu en occident. La présentation instrumentale du raga est illustrée ici par un *alap*, une composition et des *tans* composés et interprétés par Vijay Kumar Jagtap et ses étudiants.

Les ragas se rattachent au moment du jour et de la saison. Bien que le même raga puisse signifier des moments différents pour plusieurs musiciens, quelques ragas très populaires sont plus communément associés, ainsi par exemple :

bhairav au petit matin (*ré, mi♭, fa♯, sol, la, si♭, do♯, ré*)
bhupali à la fin de l'après-midi (*ré, mi, fa♯, la, si, do*)
malkauns à la pleine nuit (*ré, fa, sol, si♭, do, ré*)
miya malhar à la saison des pluies (comprenant *ré, mi, fa, sol, la, si, do* et *do♯, ré*)

Ces ragas associés à différents moments relèvent, tout comme les autres ragas, de *gharanas* ou styles vocaux divers. Toutefois, la profondeur des sentiments transmis par le musicien par l'intermédiaire de ces ragas demeure traditionnellement très forte.

Le musicologue Bhatkhande, au début du XXe siècle, voyagea dans les régions du nord de l'Inde et y recueillit de nombreux ragas et compositions qu'il répertoria. Il composa des chants didactiques appelés **lakshana geet** destinés à enseigner les caractéristiques des ragas. Il proposa également dix *thaats* ou formules de gammes très connues servant à la définition des ragas.

Nordindische
Hindustanische Musik

Dank der Großzügigkeit der Lehrer von Bharatiya Vidya Bhavan kann hier gewinnbringend für den Leser ein Überblick über den hindustanischen Raga und seine Aufführungspraxis gegeben werden.

Hindustanische Musik ist sehr stark auf die Improvisation angewiesen. Die Kompositionen sind kurze, prägnante Melodiefragmente, die die Stimmung des Ragas einfangen und dazu dienen, die Vorstellungskraft des aufführenden Musikers anzuregen. Um die Improvisationstechniken in der indischen Musik zu erlernen, geben die Lehrer ihren Studenten anleitende Beispiele, die diese nachahmen, um dann von dort aus ihren eigenen Stil zu entwickeln. Diese Schultradition nennt man Gharanas. Das zeigt vielleicht, warum der Lehrer in der Entwicklung eines indischen Musikstudenten solch eine wichtige Person ist. Die Vorstellungskraft des Studenten begründet sich auf der seines Lehrers.

Es gibt drei vokale Hauptformen:
1. **Dhrupad**, der die langsame klassische Form verkörpert, hat einen ausgedehnten improvisierten *Alap*, in dem die von der Silbe 'om' abgeleiteten Silben 'na' 'num' 'tum' verwendet werden. Danach folgt eine kurze Komposition, die einen sehr hohen literarischen Stellenwert hat, mit frommem, mystischem oder philosophischem Inhalt. Diese wird dann in unterschiedlichen Tempi wiedergegeben – doppelt, dreimal oder viermal so schnell. Das künstlerische Wagnis des Musikers und auch seine Wechselbeziehung mit dem Publikum bestimmen dabei die Tempowahl. **Dhamar**, eine besondere Art des Dhrupad, wird mit Holi assoziiert und hat immer 14 Schläge, die in 5+2+3+4 unterteilt sind. **Dhrupad** kann in unterschiedlichen Tala-Perioden stehen: 12, 18, 22, 32 und so weiter.

2. **Khyal** ist die beliebteste Form und wird in der größten Anzahl an kurzen Kompositionen in unterschiedlichen Ragas benutzt. Der **Khyal** gliedert sich in zwei Abschnitte: *Sthayi* und *Antara*. Diese bestehen üblicherweise aus je zwei Zeilen und sind mit improvisierten Abschnitten durchsetzt.

3. **Thumri** ist eine leichte klassische Form mit sehr farbenprächtigen Improvisationen, die normalerweise gegen Ende eines Konzertes gesungen wird.

Die Silben, die in den Improvisationen verwendet werden, haben ihre Wurzeln in den Gesängen der Veden. Die Instrumentation und die Handhabung der Ragas hingegen ist von den Sufimusikern und durch die Förderung des Mugalhofes beeinflusst worden. Auf der Begleit-CD führen Pandit Vishwa Prakash und seine Studenten je ein Beispiel für den Dhrupad, den Khyal und die Thumri vor. (*Alap* und *Tans* sind Improvisationen, die er für seine Studenten vorbereitet hat.)

Die Sitar ist das bekannteste indische Instrument im Westen. Auf der CD wird mit ihr der Stil einer instrumentalen Ragaaufführung gezeigt, die von Vijay Kumar Jagtap und seine Studenten komponiert und gespielt wurde. Sie besteht aus *Alap*, Komposition und *Tans*.

Ragas beziehen sich auf Zeit, und zwar sowohl auf Tages- als auch auf Jahreszeiten. Obwohl derselbe Raga für unterschiedliche Musiker auch unterschiedliche Zeiten verkörpern kann, sind einige beliebte Ragas im Großen und Ganzen festgelegt.

Zum Beispiel:
Bhairav für den frühen Morgen (D Es Fis G A B Cis D)
Bhupali für den Spätnachmittag (D E Fis A H D)
Malkauns für die Nacht (D F G B C D)
Miya Malhar für die Regenzeit (D E F G A H C und Cis D)

Ragas, die unterschiedlichen Zeiten zugeordnet werden, verändern sich je nach Gharanas oder dem Stil der Musiker, so wie alle Beschäftigung mit einem Raga diesen verändert. Dennoch bleibt die Gefühlstiefe, die der Musiker gemäß seiner Tradition durch den Raga vermittelt, sehr stark.

Zu Beginn des 20. Jahrhunderts reiste der Musikwissenschaftler Bhatkhande durch Nordindien, um viele Ragas und Ragakompostionen zu sammeln und zusammenzustellen. Er komponierte didaktische Ragalieder, **Lakshana Geet** genannt, um den Studenten die typischen Merkmale der Ragas beizubringen. Ebenso schlug er vor, die Ragas mit Hilfe von zehn *thaats* oder beliebten Tonleitermustern einzuteilen.

Dhrupad: Shankara Mahadeva

In Praise of Siva/à la louange de Shiva/Lobgesang auf Shiva

Tansen, 16th century

Rag: Darbari Kanhada Tal: Chautal–12 beats

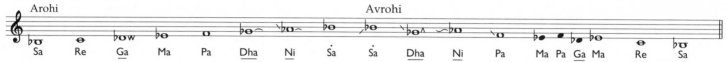

Arohi   Avrohi

Sa Re Ga Ma Pa Dha Ni Sa   Sa Dha Ni Pa Ma Pa Ga Ma Re Sa

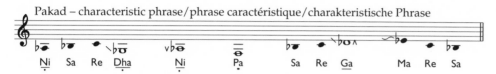

Pakad – characteristic phrase/phrase caractéristique/charakteristische Phrase

Ni Sa Re Dha Ni Pa Sa Re Ga Ma Re Sa

Sthayi

Sha – n – ka – ra Ma – ha – de – va de – va   Se – va – ka su – ra ja – ke _____

3   Antara

Sha – n – ka – ra Ma – ha – de – va de – va   bha – sma an – ga shi – sha gan – ga

5

ba – ha – na ba – li a – ti pra – cha – nda   go – ra – a – ra _ dhan – ga san – ga

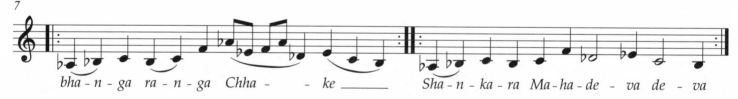

7

bha – n – ga ra – n – ga Chha – ke _____   Sha – n – ka – ra Ma – ha – de – va de – va

Sing composition in *dugan* ×2; *tigan* ×3, *chagan* ×4.

Composition vocale en *dugan* ×2, *tigan* ×3, *chagan* ×4.

Die Komposition ist folgendermaßen zu singen: *dugan* 2×; *tigan* 3×; *chagan* 4×

Chhota Khyal: Tore Meethe

Come, O Beguiling One/Viens, o toi le séduisant/Oh komm, Verführer

Pandit Lakshman Prasad Jaipure

Rag Bihag in Tal Tin Tal (16 beats)

Dance Song/chant de danse/Tanzlied

Thumri

Hori–Festival of Light/*Hori*–Fête de la lumière/Das Lichterfest

Pandit Vishwa Prakash

Rag Misra Sahana Kafi Tal Deepchandi (14 beats)

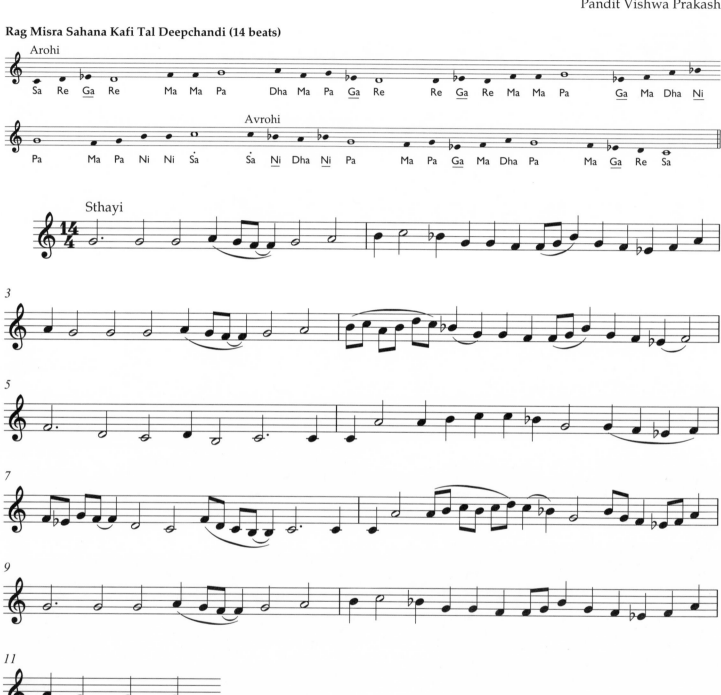

Comparative Modes and Ragas

Tableau comparatif des modes et des ragas

Vergleich von Modi und Ragas

Mode	Karnatic Melas	Hindusthani Thaat
Ionian	Sankarabharana	Bilaval
Dorian	Kharaharapriya	Kafi
Phrygian	Hanumatodi	Bhairavi
Lydian	Kalyani	Yaman
Mixolydian	Harikambhoji	Khamaj
Aeolian	Natabhairavi	Asavari
	Mayamalavagaula	Bhairov
	Subhapantuvarali	Todi
	Kamavardhini	Purva
	Gamanasrama	Marva

Hand gestures
Gestuelle manuelle/Handzeichen

Adi Tala – 8-beat
South Indian/sud de l'Inde/südindisch

The 8-beat Hand Clapping Pattern/Séquence de 8 pulsations frappée dans les mains/Klatschschema mit 8 Schlägen

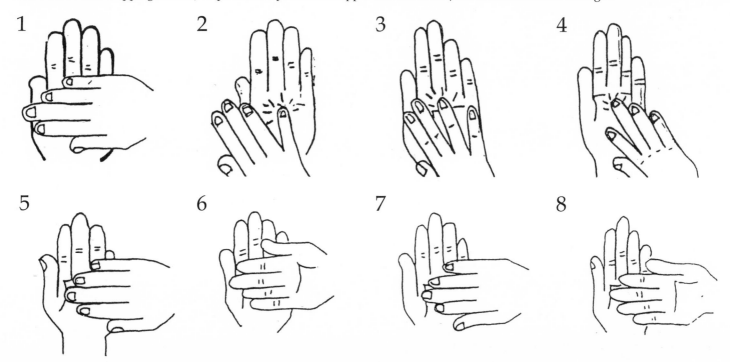

drawn by/dessins/gezeichnet von
Megan Evans, Whitbourne Primary School

Hand gestures
Gestuelle manuelle/Handzeichen

Tin Tal
North Indian/nord de l'Inde/nordindisch

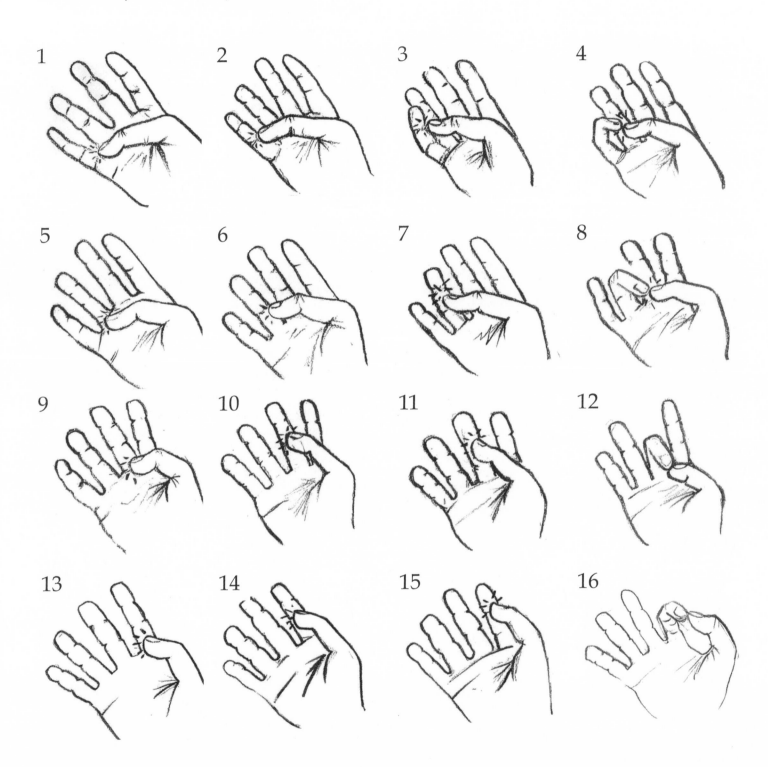

Glossary

These seven are the traditionally-taught origins:
Origine traditionnelle des septnoms de notes:
Die sieben Quellen, die traditionellerweise gelehrt werden:

1 *Shadja*	Sa, the sound of the peacock/cri du paon/der Klang des Pfau
2 *Rishabha*	Ri, the sound of the ox/cri du bœuf/der Klang des Ochsen
3 *Gandhara*	Ga, the sound of the goat/cri de la chèvre/der Klang der Ziege
4 *Madhyama*	Ma, the sound of the crane/cri du coq/der Klang des Kranichs
5 *Panchama*	Pa, the sound of the cuckoo/cri du coucou/der Klang des Kuckucks
6 *Dhaivata*	Dha, the sound of the frog/cri de la grenouille/der Klang des Frosches
7 *Nishadha*	Ni, the sound of the elephant/cri de l'éléphant/der Klang des Elefanten

H = Hindustani term/hindoustanais/hindustanischer Begriff
K = Karnatic term/carnatique/karnatischer Begriff

Alap (H)	improvisation to begin raga presentation/improvisation pour amorcer la présentation du raga/Improvisation zu Beginn einer Ragaaufführung
Alapana (K)	improvisation to begin raga presentation/improvisation pour amorcer la présentation du raga/Improvisation zu Beginn einer Ragaaufführung
Antara (H)	second theme/deuxième thème/zweites Thema
Anudrutam	1 beat/1 pulsation/1 Schlag
Anupallavi (K)	second theme/deuxième thème/zweites Thema
Arohana (K)	ascending svaras in raga/svaras ascendants du raga/aufsteigende Svaras im Raga
Arohi (H)	ascending svaras in raga/svaras ascendants du raga/aufsteigende Svaras im Raga
Audava Raga (H, K)	five-note raga/raga de cinq notes/Raga, bestehend aus fünf Noten
Avarohana (K)	descending svaras in raga/svaras descendants du raga/absteigende Svaras im Raga
Avrohi (H)	descending svaras in raga/svaras descendants du raga/absteigende Svaras im Raga
Bhajan (H)	devotional song of verse and chorus/chant religieux sous forme de versets et refrain/frommes Lied, bestehend aus Strophe und Refrain
Bhashanga Raga (K)	raga containing a foreign note/raga comportant une note étrangère/fremd – ein Raga, der eine fremde Note enthält
Bhatkhande (H)	Hindustani musicologist (1860–1936)/musicologue hindoustanais (1860–1936)/hindustanischer Musikwissenschaftler (1860–1936)
Charana (K)	third theme/troisième thème/drittes Thema
Dhrupad (H)	Classical composition form/forme classique de composition/klassische Kompositionsform
Dikshitar, Subbarama	author of *Sangita Sampradaya Pradarsini* (1839–1906)/auteur de *Sangita Sampradaya Pradarsini* (1839–1906)/Autor des Traktates *Sangita Sampradaya Pradarsini* (1839–1906)
Dikshitar, Balusvami	first violinist performer (1786–1859)/premier violoniste de concert (1786–1859)/erster südindischer Violinist (1786–1859)
Dikshitar, Muttusvami	Karnatic composer (1776–1835)/compositeur carnatique (1776–1835)/karnatischer Komponist (1776–1835)
Drutam	2 beats/2 pulsations/2 Schläge
Etrajaru (K)	ornament: upward slide/ornement : glissement ver le haut/Verzierung: aufwärtsgerichtetes Gleiten
Gamaka (H, K)	ornament/ornement/Verzierung
Gharana	singing style (usually named after the province or town in which it is sung/style chanté (généralement désigné par le nom de la province ou de la ville dont il provient)/Singstil (dieser wird normalerweise nach der Provinz oder der Stadt, in der er gesungen wird, benannt)
Gita (K)	song – beginner's piece/chant – pièce pour débutant/Lied – Stück für Anfänger
Hindustani	North Indian/du nord de l'Inde/nordindisch
Irakka jaru (K)	ornament: downwards slide/ornement : glissement vers le bas/ Verzierung: abwärtsgerichtetes Gleiten
Kampita (H, K)	ornament: shake between two notes/ornement : tremblement entre deux notes/Verzierung: Triller zwischen zwei Noten
Karnatic	South Indian/du sud de l'Inde/südindisch
Khyal (H)	composition/composition/Komposition
Kirtana (K)	Classical form of composition/forme classique de composition/klassische Kompositionsform
Komal (H)	note flattened/note abaissée/erniedrigte Note

61

Glossary

Kriti (K)	Composition, more complex/composition plus complexe/kompliziertere Komposition,
Laghu	finger-count/comptage sur les doigts/Fingerzählweise
Mridangam (K)	double ended drum/tambour à deux surfaces opposées/eine zweiseitige Trommel
Nagasvaram (K)	wind instrument - double reeded/instrument à vent à anche double/ Holzblasinstrument mit Doppelrohrblatt
Natya Sastra	Sanskrit text on Dramaturgy c. 200AD/texte sanskrit sur la dramaturgie (ca 200) Sanskrittraktat über Dramaturgie, ca. 200 n. Chr.
Nokku (K)	ornament: descending pull/ornement : note tirée descendante/Verzierung: absteigendes Ziehen
Odukkal (K)	ornament: note pushed aside, in joining two notes/ornement : note conjointe poussée de côté/Verzierung: zur Seite gedrückte Note beim Verbinden zweier benachbarter Noten
Orikkai (K)	ornament: snap, at end of a long note/ornement : claquement à fin d'une note longue/ Verzierung: schnappen, am Ende einer langen Note
Pakad (H)	characteristic phrase of the raga/phrase caractéristique du raga/ charakteristische Phrase eines Ragas
Pallavi (K)	first theme/premier thème/erstes Thema
Pratyahata (K)	ornament: 'strike back', like a mordent/ornement : comme un mordant/Verzierung: 'Rückschlag', wie ein Mordent
Purandaradasa	'Grandfather' of Karnatic music (1484–1564)/« Père » de la musique carnatique 1484-1564/ der 'Urvater' der karnatischen Musik (1484–1564)
Rag (H)	Scalar melodic pattern/dessin mélodique de gamme/tonleiterartiges Melodiemuster
Rag Bihag (H)	C♯ D F♯ G A C♯ D D C♯ B A G♯ A F♯ G E D/do♯ ré fa♯ sol la do♯ ré ré do♯ si la sol♯ la fa♯ sol mi ré/Cis D Fis G A Cis D D Cis H A Gis A Fis G E D
Rag Darbari Kanhada (H)	D E F G A B♭ C D D B♭ C G A F E D/ré mi fa sol la sib do ré ré sib do sol la fa mi ré/D E F G A B C D D B C G A F E D
Rag Misra shahana kafi (H)	D C B C A G A F G B♭ A G F E D (descending)/ré do si do la sol la fa sol sib la sol fa mi ré (descendant)/D C H C A G A F G B A G F E D (abwärts)
Rag Misra shahana kafi (H)	D E F E G G A B G A F E E F E G G A F G Bb C A G A C♯ D (ascending)/ ré mi fa mi sol sol la si sol la fa mi mi fa mi sol sol la fa sol sib do la sol la do♯ ré (ascendant')/ D E F E G G A H G A F E E F E G G A F G B C A G A Cis D (aufwärts)
Rag Ragashri (H)	B C♯ D F♯ G B C D D C♯ A F♯ E D/si do♯ ré fa♯ sol si do ré ré do♯ la fa♯ mi ré/ H Cis D Fis G H C D D Cis A Fis E D
Rag Saurashtra Bhairav (H)	D C D B C♯ D G G♯ F♯ G B G♯ B C♯ D D C♯ B A G B♭ C B♭ A F♯ G E♭ ré do ré si do♯ ré sol sol♯ fa♯ sol si sol♯ si do♯ ré ré do♯ si la sol sib do sib la fa♯ sol mi ♭/ D C D H Cis D G Gis Fis G H Gis H Cis D D Cis H A G B C B A Fis G Es
Raga (K)	Scalar melodic formula/formule mélodique de gamme/tonleiterartiges Melodiemuster
Raga Brindavani (K)	D E G A C♯ D – D C A G E D/ré mi sol la do♯ ré – ré do la sol mi ré/ D E G A Cis D – D C A G E D
Raga Garudadhvani (K)	D E F♯ G A B C♯ D – D B A F♯ E D/ré mi fa♯ sol la si do♯ ré-ré si la fa♯ mi ré D E Fis G A H Cis D – D H A Fis E D
Raga Hamsanandi (K)	D E♭ F♯ G♯ B C♯ D/ré mib fa♯ sol♯ si do♯ ré/D Es Fis Gis H Cis D
Raga Malahari (K)	D E♭ G A B♭ D – D B♭ A G F♯ E♭ D/ré mib sol la sib ré – ré sib la sol fa♯ mib ré D Es G A B D – D B A G Fis Es D
Raga Mayamalavagaula (K)	D E♭ F♯ G A B♭ C♯ D/ré mib fa♯ sol la sib do♯ ré/D Es Fis G A B Cis D
Raga Sankarabharana (K)	D E F♯ G A B C♯ D ré mi fa♯ sol la si do♯ ré/D E Fis G A H Cis D
Raga Suddha Dhanaysi (K)	D F G A C D D C A G F D/ré fa sol la do ré ré do la sol fa ré/ D F G A C D D C A G F D
Raga Suposhini (K)	D E D G A C B D – D B C A G E G E D/ré mi ré sol la do si ré – ré si do la sol mi sol mi ré D E D G A C H D – D H C A G E G E D
Ravai (K)	ornament: brief repetition of note/ornement : brève répétition d'une note/Verzierung: kurze Wiederholung der Note
Sangati (K)	a melody line repeated in more complex elaborations/ligne mélodique répétée de façon plus complexe/in komplizierteren Ausarbeitungen sich wiederholende Melodielinie
Sampurna	Complete using all 7 notes/entier, qui utilise toutes les 7 notes/vollständig, mit allen sieben Noten
Sarali varisai(K)	first exercises/premiers exercices/erste Übungen
Sarasvati	Goddess of Art and Learning/déesse de l'art et de l'instruction/Göttin der Künste und des Lernens
Shadava Raga (H, K)	six–note raga/raga de six notes/Raga, bestehend aus sechs Noten
Shahnai (H)	wind instrument – double reeded/instrument à vent à anche double/Holzblasinstrument mit Doppelrohrblatt

Glossary

Sitar (H)	string instrument – of long necked lute type//instrument à cordes : sorte de luth à long manche/Streichinstrument – eine langhalsige Lautenart
Sphurita (K)	ornament: 'throbbing' stress on the second note/ornement : accent 'lancé' sur la deuxième note/Verzierung: ´hämmernde´ Betonung auf der zweiten Note
Sthai (H)	first theme/premier thème/erstes Thema
Svarajati (K)	Rhythmic composition/composition rythmique/rhythmische Komposition
Syama Sastri (K)	Karnatic Composer (1781–1827)//compositeur carnatique (1781-1827)/ karnatischer Komponist (1781–1827)
Tabla (H)	wooden drum of tabla-bhaya set/tambour de bois de l'ensemble tabla-bhaya/hölzerne Trommel, Teil des tabla-bhaya Sets
Tal (H)	rhythm pattern/schéma rythmique/rhythmisches Muster
Tal Chautal (H)	12-beat counting pattern/schéma de 12 pulsations/Zählmuster mit 12 Schlägen
Tal Deepchandi (H)	14-beat counting pattern/schéma de 14 pulsations/Zählmuster mit 14 Schlägen
Tal Rupak (H)	7-beat counting pattern/schéma de 7 pulsations/Zählmuster mit 7 Schlägen
Tal Tin Tal (H)	16-beat counting pattern/schéma de 16 pulsations/Zählmuster mit 16 Schlägen
Tala (K)	rhythm pattern/schéma rythmique/rhythmisches Muster
Tala Adi Tala (K)	8-beat counting pattern/schéma de 8 pulsations/Zählmuster mit 8 Schlägen
Tala Dhruva (K)	14-beat counting pattern/schéma de 14 pulsations/Zählmuster mit 14 Schlägen
Tala Misra chapu (K)	7-beat counting pattern/schéma de 7 pulsations/Zählmuster mit 7 Schlägen
Tala Rupaka (K)	6-beat counting pattern/schéma de 6 pulsations/Zählmuster mit 6 Schlägen
Tans (H)	rhythmic patterns/schémas rythmiques/rhythmische Muster
Thumri (H)	light classical Hindustani song/chant classique hindoustanais léger/leichtes klassisches hindustanisches Lied
Tillana (K)	dance composition with spoken rhythm/composition de danse avec rythme parlé/ Tanzkomposition mit gesprochenem Rhythmus
Tivra (H)	note sharpened/note haussée/erhöhte Note
Tyagaraja	Karnatic composer (1767–1847)/compositeur carnatique (1767-1827)/karnatischer Komponist (1767 – 1847)
Vakra Raga (H,K)	Crooked – raga with a zig-zag movement of notes/brisé – raga aux notes en zig-zag/krumm – Raga mit einer Notenbewegung im Zick-Zack Muster
Varnam (K)	Study showing character of the raga/étude montrant le caractère du raga/Studie, die den Charakter eines Raga aufzeigt
Veda	Ancient Indian hymn collection c. 1000B.C./ancien recueil d'hymnes indiens (ca 1000 av.J.C.)/Hindu hymnologie, ca. 1000 v. Chr./altindische Hymnensammlung
Vina	String instrument – of long necked lute type, fixed frets/instrument à cordes : sorte de luth à long manche et sillets fixes/Streichinstrument – eine langhalsige Lautenart, feste Bünde

The Bharatiya Vidya Bhavan

Bharatiya Vidya Bhavan, UK Centre
4a Castletown Road,
London W14 9HE:
Tel: 020 7381 3086/4608
Website: www.bhavan.net e-mail: info@bhavan.net

The Bhavan, London centre is the largest institute engaged in teaching aspects of Indian art and culture outside India. Its courses include Indian music, dance, languages, philosophy, yoga, art and archeology. Over the years the Bhavan has established itself as the leading teaching institute in the UK for Indian music, art and culture.

There is an annual Summer School where leading artists in the field of music and dance are brought from India. The Summer School is held at the Bhavan's London premises and attracts students from all over the world.

Music Studies

- North (Hindustani) and South (Karnatic) Indian music classes
- Hindustani vocal, sitar, tabla, flute, and Bengali vocal music
- Karnatic vocal, vina, violin, mridangam and flute
- Courses at different levels: beginners, diploma (5 years), master

Courses are designed for beginners all the way to advanced players. All teachers have performing experience and most have prepared students to public performance level. The emphasis is on acquiring the practical skills of playing an instrument or singing Indian music with a background in the theoretical concepts of Indian music provided by theory classes. The courses lead to diploma qualifications.

Syllabus

The syllabus develops musical skills through exercises, compositions and improvisation structures using the framework of the raga and tala. Each year between 5 and 7 ragas are covered and 3 or 4 different talas. Student performances for celebration days each term allow the students to show their skills, and exams at the end of each year are examined by musicians from India to maintain a high standard. Bibliographies and discographies are given to support the learning.

Performances

The Bhavan regularly stages performances in its Mountbatten Auditorium along with regular workshops and lecture-demonstartions. Around one hundred performances a year are given featuring Music, Dance and Drama.

Bookshop
Books, CDs and cultural artefacts for courses are available in TEERANS the Bhavan's bookshop.

The Bhavan was established in the late 1930s with the blessings of Mahatma Gandhi to preserve the rich traditions of Indian art and culture. All people irrespective of their colour, faith and background are welcome at the Bhavan.

CD Track List

1   Tuning
2   Embellishments
3   First Exercises – Sarali varisai
4   Second Exercises – Janta varisai
5   Second Exercises – Janta varisai
6   Rhythmic Excercises – Alankara
7   First Songs – Gitam: Sri Gananatha by Purandaradasa
8   First Songs – Gitam: Padumanabha by Purandaradasa
9   European Tune: Vande Minakshi by M. Dikshitar
10 Rhythmic Song – svarajati
11 Study – Varnam by Ramanath Srinivasa Iyengar
12 Piece – Gaja Mukhanai music by T.V. Gopalakrishnan
13 Piece – Kalaivani music by T.V. Gopalakrishnan
14 Piece – Tatvameruga by Tyagaraja
15 Piece – Raminchuva by Tyagaraja
16 Piece – Sobhillu by Tyagaraja
17 Dance piece – Tillana by Dr M. Balamuralikrishna
18 Dhrupad by Tansen (i)
19 Chhota Khyal by Pandit Lakshman Prasad Jaipure (ii)
20 Thumri by Pandit Vishwa Prakash (i)
21 Sitar – Kalyani alap, jor and gat

Performers:
Karnatic Violin: Baluraghuraman with students Candida Connolly and Dhanusha Thayaparam
South Indian Percussion: Pirashanna Thevarajah mridangam, ghatam, Ganjeera and morsing

Hindustani Vocal: Pandit Vishwa Prakash,
with students   i) Praful Pate and Jyotika Dandapani
                ii) M. Shyla and Rajvi Rajani

Sitar: Vijaykumar Jagtap
with students Raaheel Husain and Anisha Babla

North Indian percussion: Rajkumar Misra (tabla)

Sound Engineer: Pammi Saib
Produced by Candida Connolly and Wendy Lampa